THE BEAUTIFUL GARDEN

and other Bible Tales

by

ELMA EHRLICH LEVINGER

Author of
Jewish Holyday Stories,
With the Jewish Child in Home and Synagogue,
In Many Lands, etc.

Illustrated by JESSIE B. ROBINSON

NEW YORK
BLOCH PUBLISHING COMPANY
1947

THESE LITTLE STORIES OF LONG AGO

ARE LOVINGLY DEDICATED

TO

GLORIA LEVINGER

For the Teacher or Parent

ALLOWING the usual number of sessions for holiday celebrations, the material in this volume should just cover a school year. The skilled teacher will find these stories suggestive for dramatization and handwork.

The pre-school child will love the pictures and should enjoy hearing the stories read. Because of the repetition he will soon be able to read them himself. Even in the home, he will enjoy "acting out" his favorite tales or fashioning a paper ark or basket for the infant Moses. At least my own children did!

ELMA EHRLICH LEVINGER

New York City, 1945

▾

Contents

INTRODUCTION   ix

THE BEAUTIFUL GARDEN   1

THE FIRST RAINBOW   9

THE GIVING OF ISAAC   15

THE GIRL AT THE WELL   22

A LADDER THAT REACHED TO HEAVEN   30

HOW JACOB WON HIS WIFE   35

THE BOY WHO HAD STRANGE DREAMS   42

FROM A PRISON TO A THRONE   49

JOSEPH AND HIS BROTHERS   56

MOSES IN THE BULRUSHES   64

THE PRINCE WHO BECAME A SHEPHERD   68

THE BURNING BUSH   73

BEFORE THE THRONE OF PHARAOH   77

THE DANCE BY THE SEA   84

THE BEGINNING OF THE LONG LONG JOURNEY   87

THE CHILDREN OF ISRAEL RECEIVE THE TEN COMMAND-
     MENTS   90

MOSES LEAVES HIS PEOPLE   96

AND DOWN FELL JERICHO!   102

THE STRONGEST MAN WHO EVER LIVED   106

THE GIRL WITH THE FAITHFUL HEART   114

THE VOICE IN THE DARKNESS   120

A KING OVER ISRAEL   127

THE SHEPHERD BOY FROM BETHLEHEM   130

THE WISEST OF KINGS   137

ELIJAH THE GOOD PROPHET   144

THE MAN WHO TRIED TO RUN AWAY FROM GOD   152

HOW GOD SAVED A GOOD MAN FROM THE LIONS   158

A JEWISH GIRL SAVES HER PEOPLE   163

Introduction

ELMA EHRLICH LEVINGER has turned her great talent for story-telling to the immortal tales of the Bible and has produced a book of charm and appeal. The parent or teacher who wishes to introduce a child to the pages of the Bible, familiar and beloved among adults, will be grateful for this book.

Out of the treasure-house of Bible narratives, Mrs. Levinger has selected stories of some of the best-known personalities of early Israel, and she has recounted their experiences with her customary skill and understanding. Children will be delighted to hear these stories read to them by others and they will rejoice also to read them for themselves.

Mrs. Levinger has prepared these narratives with pedagogical wisdom, with command over vital and picturesque phrase, and with keen perception of their ethical instruction. She has avoided obvious moralization but the spiritual lessons of the Bible tales are nonetheless forcibly evoked and interpreted. The words are simple; the imagery vivid; the creative material, built upon the foundation of the biblical text, has artistic accuracy, and the total effect is captivating for young and old alike.

The author shows anew the universal attraction of the Bible narratives and it is certain that these stories will meet with applause by readers of all faiths. The Bible heroes, with all their virtues and foibles, live again in Mrs. Levinger's book. Hosts of children who will make their acquaintance for the first time through the pages of her volume will be deeply indebted to her, and multitudes of parents and teachers in the home, the school and the community, will rise up and call her their mentor and friend.

LOUIS I. NEWMAN

New York, July, 1945

The Beautiful Garden

ONCE upon a time God planted a beautiful garden and called it Eden. It was in a faraway land across the waters. From that day to this no one has ever seen such a lovely place as the Garden of Eden. Tall trees grew in this garden and bright flowers. The trees never dropped their leaves and the flowers never faded, for it was always summer there.

Birds with gay feathers sang in the tree tops. On the soft grass all sorts of animals played together, rabbits and squirrels and busy little chipmunks. There were woolly lambs and big-eyed cows. There were also lions and tigers. But in this faraway Garden of Eden there were no cages. Because this was such a wonderful garden the big and strong animals were all tame. They went wherever they pleased and the lambs and cows were not afraid of them.

Before God planted the garden He made the sky with the sun to give light in the daytime and the moon and all the stars to shine at night. He made the rivers and the lakes and the big, blue oceans. He made the earth with all the trees and flowers, the animals and the fish and the birds. Then He created the first Man and Woman to enjoy all the pleasant things which He had made.

The name of the first man was Adam and his wife God called Eve. They were the only people in the whole world. God put them in the Garden of Eden where at first they were very happy. They enjoyed the beautiful flowers. Adam named the animals which were all tame and friendly. Adam's pet was a great yellow lion with a long, silky mane. But Eve liked the rabbits best and a tiny lamb which followed her wherever she went.

There was plenty to eat because the trees and the bushes were always covered with fruits or berries. In the middle of the garden grew a tree loaded with bright, ripe fruit.

God told Adam and Eve they might eat all the fruit they wanted from every other tree. But He said: "You must not eat the fruit of this tree in the middle of the garden. You must not even touch the tree. I know I can trust you to obey Me."

"We will obey You, God," promised Adam and Eve. "We will never even touch this tree. You have given us all the fruit we can eat and it tastes very good. So why would we want any fruit from this tree?"

For many days Adam and Eve kept their promise.

The songs of the birds woke them early every morning. Adam and his wife would breakfast on fruits and berries. Then they took a long walk through the garden. The garden was so big they never reached the end of it. When they were tired, they would sit down to rest under a shady tree. Adam liked to make pipes out of the willows which grew along the river. He played upon his pipe so sweetly that all the animals came about him to listen.

Eve liked to make chains of flowers. She picked only the biggest and reddest roses and tied them with buttercups and violets. She would bind them about her long golden hair. Sometimes just for fun she would put a wreath around the neck of her pet lamb.

One afternoon Adam went down to the river to swim. Eve felt too lazy and sleepy to go with him. She lay on the soft grass and looked up through the branches of the trees to the soft blue sky. She was half asleep when she heard a rustling in the bushes. She thought it was her pet lamb or some of the rabbits. The bunnies liked to cuddle up close beside her when she took her afternoon nap. But it was a long green Snake with big black eyes that had wound itself around a tree.

"Good afternoon, Eve," said the Snake politely. (I forgot to tell you that in this fairy garden all of the animals could really talk.)

"Good afternoon," answered Eve.

"Do you want me to show you something wonderful?" asked the Snake. He began to slide down from the tree.

Eve sat up. "Shall I call Adam?" she asked. "He may want to see it, too."

"No," said the Snake crossly, "I don't want Adam tagging along."

"How sweet the honeysuckle smells!" said Eve, stopping to pick a spray.

"Can't you hurry a little?" asked the Snake, crosser than ever.

Eve did not know he was afraid that Adam might come up from the river any minute and spoil his plan.

They stopped before a tree. Its branches were so heavy with bright, ripe fruit that they trailed on the ground. "This is what I wanted to show you," said the Snake.

"Is that all you wanted to show me? What a silly old Snake you are," Eve laughed. "The very first day we were in this garden God showed us this tree."

"It is different from all the other trees in the garden," said the Snake.

"I know it is," answered Eve. "I don't know what makes it different. But God said we must not eat its fruit or even touch it."

"That sounds very silly to me," said the Snake. "If I were you, I'd do as I pleased."

"But Adam and I can do anything else we please," said Eve. "We can eat fruit from all the other trees. Why should we taste the fruit from this one?"

"You are just afraid God will punish you," teased the Snake. "But He will never know if you take just one piece of fruit and taste it."

"Maybe if I took only one little piece," said Eve. "I don't know why but I would rather have just a bite of the fruit from this tree than from any other tree in the whole garden."

Very slowly Eve reached her hand out toward one of the lower branches. She drew back; reached for the fruit, drew back again.

Eve slowly pulled off a piece of fruit and bit into it. It tasted very, very good. She took another bite.

Just then Adam pushed through the vines of honeysuckle and walked over to the tree. Eve knew she was doing wrong and felt ashamed. She tried to eat the rest of the fruit in her hand before Adam could see it.

"What are you doing, Eve?" asked Adam.

Eve had been eating so fast that now she choked a little. She could not answer him. Adam leaned over and saw the bit of fruit she tried to hide in her hand.

"Eve," he said. "God told us not even to touch this tree."

"I never tasted any fruit like this," said Eve. "Won't you take a bite?"

"I will not eat it and disobey God," said Adam.

But when Eve dropped the fruit into his hand, it smelled so good he could not bear to throw it away. "If I eat just this little bit you have left, God will never know," said Adam. He ate the rest of the fruit. Then he also felt ashamed and afraid for he knew that he had done wrong to break his promise and disobey God.

They walked slowly back to their favorite spot under the trees. Adam began to play his pipe. Some little monkeys swung down from the branches and tried to dance. But Adam did not feel like laughing at them as they tumbled about. Eve picked up the wreath of flowers she had left there. But she did not want to finish it. When her pet lamb came up and rubbed against her shoulder, she pushed him crossly away.

The sun began to set. The air of the garden grew cool and smelled sweeter than ever. Then from far off Adam and Eve heard God's voice.

"Adam!" called God. And when Adam didn't answer He spoke again: "Adam!"

For the first time Adam was afraid to talk to God. He did not know that God sees everywhere and we can never hide from Him. Adam took Eve's hand and they ran as fast as they could and hid in some thick bushes. Again they heard God calling to them.

"Adam," said God's voice, "where are you?"

Then Adam knew he could not hide from God. He came out from the bushes and pulled Eve after him.

"Why did you hide?" God asked.

"I heard Your voice," said Adam, "and I was afraid."

"Why were you afraid?" asked God. "You have never been afraid of Me before."

"I was afraid You would be angry with me," said Adam.

"Did you eat of the forbidden tree?" God asked.

"Yes," said Adam. "Eve gave me a bit of the fruit and I ate it. And she ate some of the fruit also."

"Why did you disobey Me and pick the fruit, Eve?" asked God.

"The Snake said I might eat it," Eve told God.

"I will punish the Snake," said God. "From this day he will be hated by all the other animals. When you have children, they will hate the Snake, too. And I must punish you and Adam also. As long as you were good and obedient, you could be happy in My beautiful garden. But now you must both go out into the wide world. You do not deserve to live here any more."

Then God sent Adam and Eve out into the wide world. There were heavy golden gates at the east end of the Garden of Eden. God closed the gates and set before them Angels with flaming swords.

So from that day to this no man has ever been able to visit the place where Adam and Eve were so happy. And to this day no one has ever found the way back to the beautiful, faraway Garden of Eden.

The First Rainbow

LONG, long ago there lived a man named Noah. He was a good man and taught his three sons to be good also. But all of the other people upon the earth except Noah and his family were very wicked and did not obey God.

Then God spoke to Noah and said: "Everyone on earth has grown so wicked except you and your family that I must drown all of them. But because you and your wife and your sons and their families are good, I will save all of you from the flood of waters I am sending down on the earth. So you must make a large Ark. This boat must be large enough for you and your whole family and two of every kind of animal and bird that is now alive."

Noah asked his sons to help him and they built a large Ark. First Noah's wife and the wives of his three sons went on board. Then Noah and his sons drove the animals, two of every kind, into the pens that were built in the lower part of the boat. This was a hard thing to do because the elephants took up so much room and the donkeys didn't want to move and had to be pushed along. The sheep and goats were frightened and gave Noah a long chase; but the camels did not seem a bit afraid.

Noah's wife had two pet cats; they kept climbing out of their pen as often as Noah put them in. So they were allowed to go up to stay in the cabin with Noah's family. Of course, Noah's two hunting dogs stayed in the cabin too. Noah gave each of them an extra bone for supper that night because they had helped him drive the animals into the Ark.

Noah's wicked neighbors, who had always laughed at him for obeying God, stood in front of the Ark and teased him. Noah was not angry with them; he was only sorry they were going to be punished because he was a very kind man.

"What are you going to do with that great big boat?" asked Noah's neighbors. "You will never get it down to the river."

"Haven't I told you again and again," Noah answered patiently, "that very soon God will send so much rain that the whole world will be covered with water?"

Everybody laughed. "That will have to be a mighty big rain," they said.

"It will be the biggest rain since the world began," Noah told them. "And God says that it will rain for forty days and for forty nights."

Everybody laughed harder than ever. "If it rains so long we will have to stay in our houses," they said. "But we will keep our animals in the barns. We always knew you were a foolish man. Now we know you are really crazy to take all those birds and beasts to live with you."

While the wicked people were still laughing and teasing Noah, the rain began to fall. It rained so hard that everybody ran home. Noah closed all the windows in the Ark. He fed the birds and animals. Then he went up to the cabin to have supper with his family. Noah's wife began to scold her youngest grandchild for spilling his milk.

"You must not speak so crossly," Noah told her. "If we must all live close together for forty days and forty nights, we must be kind and friendly and not quarrel."

Noah's wife told him she was sorry she had been so cross. After that there was no more scolding or quarreling in the cabin. But the animals were not so good. Especially the monkeys. They began to scold and chatter at each other on the first day of the rain and they were never quiet (except when they were asleep, of course) as long as the flood lasted.

At first the Ark did not move. But it rained and rained and rained until the whole earth was covered with water. First the water covered the houses and the trees. Then it rose to the tops of the hills. At last even the high mountains were under water and what had once been the earth looked like a great, wide sea. But the Ark floated upon the top of the waters. Everyone in it was safe just as God had promised Noah.

Then the rain stopped as suddenly as it had started. Noah opened one of the cabin windows and looked out. The sun was shining warm and bright. But Noah could see nothing but water all around him.

Noah had a big black raven which was a very clever bird. Noah called the raven to him and told it to fly out across the waters to see whether it could spy any dry land. The raven croaked that it would come back as soon as it could. But Noah never saw the bird again.

Then Noah sent a gentle white dove across the wide waters. He closed the cabin window again; but soon he heard a gentle peck-pecking outside. Noah opened the window and the dove come in, wet and shivering.

Then Noah was sure that the waters were still very high and he waited another seven days before he sent the dove away again.

Soon there was a gentle peck-pecking outside. Noah opened the window and the dove flew in and sat upon his shoulder. Then Noah saw that in her mouth she carried a fresh leaf from an olive tree. Noah knew that olive trees are very low. He was sure that if the dove was able to reach an olive tree the waters must be drying very fast. He was sure that this was a sign that the flood was over. He thanked the gentle dove and blessed her.

Noah and his sons and their families began to pack up everything they had brought to make themselves comfortable in the Ark. In their pens below the lions roared and the bears growled and the monkeys chattered. They were all tired of staying in the Ark so long and wanted to get out on dry land. The birds that Noah had saved from the flood, two of every kind that flies, sang a song of praise to God. But the gentle dove would not leave Noah's shoulder. She sat there and cooed with joy.

As soon as Noah left the Ark with his family, he built an altar. He made a fire on the altar and roasted meat upon it. This was called a burnt-offering. In those long-ago days people did this when they wanted to thank God for being good to them. So Noah and his sons and their families thanked God for saving them from the flood.

Then God spoke to Noah.

He said: "From this day there shall be seedtime and harvest, and cold and heat, and summer and winter, and sunshine and rain. I will send rain from the skies to make the grass green and to water what men shall plant in their fields. But I will never again send a flood to cover the earth."

"Look, Grandpa!" Noah's youngest grandson cried out.

Everyone turned to look. Across the sky stretched a lovely rainbow. Its ends seemed to touch the earth.

"Noah," said God, "I have set My bow in the clouds. Sometimes there will be a long, long rain and you may grow afraid. But I promise you that after the rain the sun will shine again. And when you see the rainbow in the heavens, you will always remember My promise to you this day."

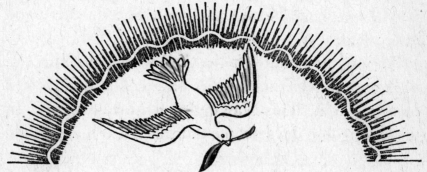

The Giving of Isaac

THERE was once a time when angels talked with men. Abraham and his wife, Sarah, lived in Palestine. Abraham was the father of the Jewish people. Abraham was very rich. He had cattle and silver and gold. But he was not happy.

Abraham and Sarah had no children. Abraham often said to Sarah: "God has promised me that I will be the father of a great people. He has said that my grandchildren's children will rule this land. God told me there would be so many of them that they could not be counted. He said there would be as many of my people living in Palestine as there are grains of sand on the sea shore and stars in the sky."

"But how can this happen?" asked Sarah. "For we are both very old and I have never had even one child." She began to cry and Abraham tried to comfort her.

One summer day Abraham sat under the great oak tree that stood near the door of his tent. He saw three men coming toward him. They were strangers.

Abraham ran to meet them. "Come and sit down and rest in the shade of this tree," he said. "You must be very hot. I will bring you water to wash with. And I will give you something to eat."

The three strangers thanked Abraham for his kindness. They sat down to rest in the cool shade of the oak tree. They took off their shoes and Abraham poured water on their hot, tired feet. Then he put a good meal before them and they ate everything he brought for they were very hungry.

While the strangers ate, Sarah came to the door of the tent to look at them.

"You have been very kind to us," said the oldest and tallest stranger. "You are a good man and I am glad you are going to be so happy. You have cattle and silver and gold. But you do not feel rich. You feel poor because you do not have a son. I know that God will send you that blessing, too."

Sarah was sure that she would never have a baby.

The stranger's words sounded so foolish to her that she began to laugh.

The strangers thanked Abraham for his kindness. Abraham stood under the big oak tree and watched them as they walked down the twisted, dusty path. He did not know that angels had visited him.

God kept his promise to Abraham and sent him a son.

"What shall we name the baby?" Abraham asked Sarah.

"Let us call him Isaac," answered Sarah. "The word Isaac means laughter. You remember how I laughed at the angel who brought me God's promise? And now I am laughing because I am so happy."

Isaac grew up into a fine strong boy. Sarah and Abraham were very proud of him.

In Abraham's time people often made a burnt-offering. Farmers wanted to thank God for sending rain and sunshine to make the trees grow. They would build an altar and place their best fruit upon it. When they roasted a goat for a family feast, the father of the family would roast some of it on the altar. He thanked God for sending him good things to eat. He wanted to share them with God.

Abraham often made burnt-offerings. It was his way of thanking God for all his blessings.

One day God's voice came to Abraham.

God said: "Abraham, take your only son, Isaac, whom I have given you, to the mountains. Build an altar and place him upon it. He shall be a burnt-offering."

Abraham began to cry. He loved Isaac very much. How could he bear to kill him? He did not want to give him up even to please God.

Early the next morning Abraham saddled his donkey. He told Sarah that he was going to take Isaac into the mountains but he did not tell her why. Sarah gave them a flask of water and some bread and dates to eat on the way. She kissed Isaac goodbye and told Abraham to take good care of him.

Spring is very beautiful in Palestine. Abraham was sure that he had never seen such a lovely morning. The dew was still bright upon the flowers along the twisted path. Birds sang in every tree.

Isaac helped his father to cut some wood which they loaded on the donkey's back. Abraham led the donkey and Isaac walked beside his father. The boy felt so happy that he began to sing a little song his mother had taught him. Isaac wondered why his father looked so sad.

At night they wrapped themselves in their long cloaks and lay down to sleep under a tree. Early the next morning they started to walk again. They walked for two days more. They ate the food Sarah had prepared for them and slept at night under a tree. On the morning of the third day Abraham saw the path leading up the mountain side. He knew this was the mountain God had chosen.

Abraham told Isaac to tie the donkey to a tree. He told Isaac to take the wood and follow him up the mountain side. Abraham carried a flint to light the fire and a knife. Isaac had often seen his father use the knife when he killed a lamb or a calf for a burnt-offering.

They began to climb the mountain. They had to walk slowly because the path was steep. The wood was heavy and Isaac soon grew tired. He stopped to rest.

"Father," he said, "I do not understand."

"What don't you understand, my son?" asked Abraham.

"I am carrying the wood," answered Isaac. "And you have the flint to make the fire. But where is the calf or lamb for the burnt-offering."

Abraham could not answer him. He went on climbing the mountain. Isaac, with the wood on his shoulder, followed him. So both of them walked together.

They came to a clearing in the thick bushes which grew along the mountain side. Suddenly Abraham knew this was the place where God wanted him to build an altar.

Abraham told his son to put down the wood. Together they gathered some large flat stones. Together they built the altar and put the wood upon it.

Isaac could not understand why his father was crying.

"Father," he asked again, "where is the lamb for the burnt-offering?"

Abraham had always obeyed God. He could not understand why God had asked him to do this. But he knew he must obey.

He tied Isaac's hands and feet with some rope he had brought with him and laid him upon the altar. Then Abraham took the knife from his belt.

It was very still up there on the side of the mountain. Not a bird sang. Even the wind was quiet in the trees. Then God's voice came through the quiet.

God said: "Abraham, do not hurt your child. I asked you to give him to Me because I know you love him better than anything else in the whole world. I wanted to know whether you would obey Me."

Then Abraham understood that God had only wanted to test him. He told Isaac not to be frightened any more. Abraham cut the ropes with the knife he had brought with him. He lifted Isaac from the altar and kissed him.

"You are a good child," Abraham said to Isaac. "You have obeyed me this day as I was ready to obey God."

Abraham heard a rustling in the bushes. It looked like a sheep. Yes, it was a big mountain ram. His horns were caught in the low branches of a tree and he could not get away.

"My child," said Abraham to his son, "see the burnt-offering God has sent us."

Abraham killed the ram and laid him on the altar. He lit the fire and watched the smoke rise toward the sky. Isaac stood beside him.

Abraham and Isaac came down from the mountain. They untied the donkey. They took turns riding him. As they started on the path toward home Isaac began to sing again. He sang a song his mother Sarah had taught him.

The Girl at the Well

Abraham was now very, very old. His wife Sarah was dead. Abraham knew that soon he would die also. He did not want to leave Isaac alone in the world.

Isaac was now a strong, tall young man. Abraham wanted him to be married. Then he would have a wife to take care of him and comfort him when Abraham died.

Abraham had a servant named Eliezer. Eliezer took care of Abraham's household. Eliezer told all the other servants what to do. He saw that Abraham's many sheep and goats had enough to eat. Abraham trusted him in all things.

One day Abraham called Eliezer to him "Eliezer," said Abraham, "I am very old. I know that I shall die soon. I want your young master, Isaac, to have a loving wife to comfort him when I am gone. I want Isaac's wife to come from my own people who live far from this place. I want you to visit my brother Nahor. Tell him I want you to bring back one of his daughters. She shall be the wife of my only son, Isaac."

"My master," answered Eliezer, "I have always tried to serve you well. Now I am glad to take this long, hard journey for your sake. But what shall I do if your brother does not wish to send his daughter back with me? What will I do if his daughter is afraid to go with me to a strange and faraway land?"

"Then I shall not blame you," answered Abraham "But I know God will help you to do the thing I have asked you to do."

Then Eliezer chose three servants to go with him. He took ten of Abraham's best camels. He loaded them with food and water for the long journey and many rich gifts for the family of Nahor, who was Abraham's brother.

It was a long, long journey. At last Eliezer reached the town on the edge of the desert where Nahor, the brother of Abraham, lived. It was just sunset. Eliezer was so stiff and tired from riding that he could hardly move. He slid from the back of his camel. The camel shook his shaggy head from side to side and grunted. Eliezer knew what that meant: the poor animal was very thirsty. The other nine camels began to toss and shake their heads and grunt and whine. They were thirsty too.

Eliezer hurried to make them comfortable. He had them kneel down and loosened the ropes which held the saddle bags on their backs. He was glad to see a well at the town gate.

"First I will give my poor, tired camels a drink," said Eliezer to himself. "Then I will go to Nahor's house. But suppose I cannot coax him to let his daughter go back with me? And what will I do if she does not want to come? Or suppose he has several daughters and I choose the wrong one for Isaac's wife!"

Then Eliezer remembered that Abraham, his master, had promised that God would help him do this hard thing. So Eliezer asked God to help him.

Eliezer prayed: "O Lord, the God of my master Abraham, help me this day! I will speak to one of the maidens who have come down to the well to draw water. I will say: Fill your pitcher with water that I may drink. And if she is the maiden who should marry Isaac, let her answer: Drink, and I will give your camels to drink, also."

Then Eliezer walked over to the well. A girl came down the path carrying a large clay water jug upon her head. Eliezer saw that she was young and very beautiful. She let the bucket down into the well and filled her pitcher. She placed the pitcher upon her head and stood talking to several other young girls who had come to draw water from the well. When she turned to leave Eliezer spoke to her.

"Will you give me a little water from your pitcher?" asked Eliezer.

"Come away, Rebecca," whispered one of the girls, pulling her sleeve. "He is a stranger and looks wild and dirty. Come away!"

"Aren't you ashamed to treat a stranger so?" answered Rebecca. "You'd look dirty, too, if you took a long ride across the desert." She held the pitcher out to Eliezer. She bowed politely and said, "Drink, my lord."

Eliezer thanked her and drank eagerly. While he drank, he said to himself: "I hope this is the girl God wants me to bring back for Isaac's wife. For she is as good and kind as she is beautiful."

"How tired and hot your poor camels look!" said Rebecca. "I am sure they are very thirsty. I will draw for the camels and give them all the water they want."

Rebecca filled her pitcher again and began to fill the long stone trough that stood near the well. Eliezer brought the camels up, one by one, and let them drink. One of the girls began to laugh.

"Have you nothing better to do, Rebecca," she asked, "than to draw water for all the camels that stop at the gates?"

"The poor animals are thirsty and I am glad to serve them," answered Rebecca.

Eliezer thanked God in his heart for answering his prayer. This girl was as kind and good as she was beautiful; she was kind even to the ugly, cross camels. But what would he do if she did not belong to Abraham's family?

"Whose daughter are you?" he asked.

Rebecca answered him: "I am the daughter of Bethuel, the son of Nahor."

Eliezer was very happy. Rebecca was not only beautiful and kind but she was the grandaughter of Nahor, Abraham's brother!

"Blessed be the Lord, the God of my master Abraham, Who has led me to the house of my master's family!" cried Eliezer.

Eliezer drew a little bag from his belt. From it he took a heavy ring of pure gold and two beautiful bracelets. He put the ring upon Rebecca's finger and the bracelets upon her wrists. Rebecca drew back. She was afraid her father would scold her for taking such rich gifts from a stranger.

"It is not right for me to take these rich gifts," she said.

"It is right for you to have them," answered Eliezer "For they were sent to you by my master Abraham. Take me to your house and I will tell you why I have come."

When Eliezer came to Rebecca's house, her brother Laban helped make the camels comfortable for the night. Eliezer gave the beasts food; he loosened their saddle bags. Then he went into the house.

Rebecca and her mother set food and drink before Eliezer. But he said: "I will not eat until I have told you why I have come."

"Yes, tell us why my brother Abraham sent you," answered Nahor.

Then Eliezer told them all how Abraham had made him promise to try to bring back a girl from his own family for Isaac's wife. He told also how he had prayed at the well for God to help him find a good wife for the young master. And he told them all how Rebecca had spoken exactly as he had hoped she would.

"Now tell me," said Eliezer, "will you deal kindly with my master Abraham and make him happy by giving the maiden, Rebecca, to Isaac for his wife?"

Laban and Bethuel answered him. "It is the Lord's wish," they said. "Rebecca stands before you. Take her and go, and let her be the wife of your master's son."

Eliezer spread out upon the table the silver and the

gold and the beautiful clothes Abraham had sent to his brother, Nahor, and the rest of his family. He gave Rebecca a necklace of gold, a band of gold to bind the veil about her head, and gold earrings to wear in her ears. They had a great feast and everyone wished that Rebecca would be happy in her new home.

The next morning Rebecca and several servants and her nurse, who had taken care of her from the time she was a baby, dressed for the long journey. Eliezer brought the camels before the door. The camels kneeled down and Rebecca and her old nurse and the servants got upon their backs. Then Eliezer got upon the back of the camel which led all the others.

All of Rebecca's family and the servants followed her to the gate. They blessed her and prayed that God would make her happy in her new home. They asked God to give her strong and brave sons. They called goodbye until the camels were so far off they looked like black spots against the desert sky.

Eliezer rode beside Rebecca. He told her how when Abraham died his son Isaac would be the richest man in the whole country. He told her also how kind and gentle Isaac was. Eliezer said he knew that Rebecca would sometimes be lonely for her own people. But he said that Isaac would be so good to her that she would be happy.

At last they reached the end of the journey. It was

early evening. Eliezer pointed out to Rebecca the great oak tree that stood before Abraham's tent.

"We are almost home," he said.

"Who is that man walking in the field?" asked Rebecca.

"It is my young master, Isaac," answered Eliezer. "He must be so anxious to see you that he has come out to meet us."

A Ladder that Reached to Heaven

ISAAC and Rebecca had twin sons. Their names were Esau and Jacob. Esau was wild and restless. He became a hunter. He never stayed at home. But Jacob loved his home. He liked to take care of the sheep and cattle. He helped his father all he could. When Isaac grew sick and old, Jacob tried to take his place. Jacob began to tell the servants what to do. He was kind to them and they all loved him.

One day Rebecca said to Isaac: "You know you once promised Jacob that when you die he will have all your gold and silver and sheep and cattle. He will take good care of everything just as he does now. When he marries he will teach his sons to be good men. But I do not want him to marry a woman like Esau's wife. She is a woman of Canaan. We are already ashamed of her wild children."

"Whom do you want Jacob to marry?" asked Isaac.

"Your father, Abraham, would not let you marry a woman of this country," answered Rebecca. "Don't you remember how he sent his good servant to my father's house? Your father wanted you to marry a girl from his brother's family. Why don't you send Jacob to visit my brother, Laban? He has two daughters and I am sure one of them will make Jacob a good wife."

Isaac called Jacob to him and told him to get ready for a long journey.

"I am very old and sick," said Isaac, "and soon I shall die. Then you will be ruler of the household in my place. You will be very rich. Your family will be one of the strongest in the land of Canaan. God promised your grandfather, Abraham, many years ago that our family would grow until there would be as many of our people as the sands on the sea shore and stars in the sky. God said that we would bless all the people of the earth by our good deeds.

"But," went on Isaac, "you must have a wife to teach your sons to be good men. I do not want you to marry a woman of Canaan. She might be like your brother

Esau's wife. I want you to do what I did. Take a wife from the family of Abraham. Go to your Uncle Laban's land and ask him to give you one of his daughters for your wife."

Jacob picked out the best of his father's servants to look after the household while he was away. He packed some food and drink and gifts for his uncle's family on the back of a little grey donkey. Then he kissed his father and mother goodbye and set out on his long journey.

He journeyed all day. When the sun set he camped by the side of the road for the night. He gave his donkey water from a little brook that ran among the tall grass. Jacob tied the little animal to a tree. He made the rope very long. He knew the donkey was hungry and would like to eat the dewy grass. Then he bathed in the brook and ate his own supper.

There were many ants and bugs in the tall grass. Jacob was afraid that they might get into his ears while he slept. So he took a big stone for a pillow. It was dark and lonely and Jacob had never been so far from home in all his life. But he prayed that God would take care of him.

He was so tired that he fell asleep at once. Suddenly he seemed to see a great ladder that reached from the ground up to the sky. The ladder shone and sparkled in the darkness. It seemed to be made of hundreds and hundreds of bright little stars. Jacob looked at the ladder; he was almost afraid to breathe. As he looked tall white angels came down the ladder. Their brightness drove away the darkness.

Then God spoke to Jacob. "I am the Lord, the God of Abraham and the God of Isaac. I will give the land where you are sleeping to you; I will give it to you and your children forever. Some day their children will be a great people. They will spread to the west and to the east, and to the north, and to the south. In your family all the families of the earth will be blessed. I will always take care of them. Never be afraid again for I will never leave you."

The angels began to move slowly up the ladder toward the heavens. For a moment the ladder stood empty. It shone like hundreds and hundreds of bright stars. Then it faded slowly away.

Jacob sat up and looked about him. It was all darkness again.

"Surely," Jacob said, "the Lord is in this place. This is the house of God and this is the gate of heaven."

He fell asleep again. He was not afraid any more. He knew that God would take care of him even if he was far from home.

Early the next morning Jacob woke up. He was rested and ready for the rest of his long journey. But before he left the place he poured oil upon the stone which had been his pillow. This made it an altar to God.

"I will call this place Beth-El," said Jacob, "because it is the House of God. I know God will take care of me on the road. When I come back in peace to my father's house I will stop here again and thank God for all His goodness to me."

Then Jacob climbed upon his donkey's back and rode toward the land where his Uncle Laban lived. He did not know how many years would pass until he came back again to the place where he had seen the shining ladder and had heard God's voice.

How Jacob Won his Wife

JACOB journeyed on and on until he reached the gates of the town where his Uncle Laban lived. In a field nearby he saw a well covered with a great stone. Three flocks of sheep crowded about the well. The sheep ran here and there; they pushed each other and jumped over each other's backs. They all tried to get to the well for they were all very thirsty.

Three boys ran here and there, pushing the sheep about and trying to get the animals into their own flock. The boys wore short robes; each carried a long staff in his hand. They were shepherds.

The shepherds took the stone from the low well.

Each in his turn took his own sheep to the well and let them drink. Then they covered the well and started to drive the sheep to their pastures.

Jacob spoke to the shepherds.

"My brothers," he said, "do you know Laban, the son of Bethuel?"

"Of course we know him," answered the shepherds. "If you want to go to his house, stranger, his youngest daughter Rachel will show you the way. Look, she is coming with her flock to give them water at the well."

Jacob looked where they pointed and saw Rachel driving the sheep before her. She was the most beautiful girl he had ever seen. Now he was glad that his father had sent him to marry one of Laban's daughters.

He ran to the well and lifted up the heavy stone that the sheep might drink. Then he told her that he was the son of her Aunt Rebecca in faraway Canaan. She welcomed him gladly and when the sheep had all been watered she took him to her father's house.

At the door of Laban's house stood Leah, his older daughter. Her face was dark and cross. Jacob thought she was not half so beautiful and sweet as her sister, Rachel.

Laban welcomed Jacob. He told his daughters to bring cool water that Jacob might bathe after his long, hot journey, He gave Jacob clean, fresh clothes to wear and told the two girls to set food and drink before their cousin. While Jacob ate and drank he told his uncle all about his father and his mother back in Canaan. Jacob said that his father was now old and sick; he told Laban that Jacob wished him to take a wife before he died.

Jacob's uncle begged him to stay with him for a long visit. So Jacob lived with Laban and his daughters for a whole month. Leah was always busy with caring for the house; she baked the bread and swept the floors and she wove cloth and made clothing for everyone in the household. But Rachel liked better to work out of doors. Every day she took the sheep to the well to drink. Then she would drive them to the pasture that they might eat the fresh, rich grass.

Jacob always went with her. As they sat on a little hill and watched the sheep, Jacob would tell Rachel of his home in Canaan. He told her of his father's riches which made Isaac a strong man in the land. He spoke also of God's promise to make him the father of a great people.

Rachel listened to all that Jacob said. When he told her he loved her and wanted her to be his wife, Rachel answered that she loved him also and would be glad to follow him back to Canaan.

At the end of the month, Laban said to Jacob: "For a whole month you have helped Rachel to take care of the sheep. I should pay you for working as my shepherd. What wages do you want?"

"I do not want any wages," answered Jacob. "I will be glad to work for you without pay if you will give me Rachel for my wife."

"How long will you work for me if I give you Rachel for your wife?" asked Laban.

"Will a year be enough?" asked Jacob.

"No indeed!" answered Laban. He was a clever man and he always made a hard bargain. "I love my daughter Rachel very much. I do not want her to marry you and leave me in a year. But if you will work for me seven years I will give her to you as your wife."

"I will serve you seven years if you will give me Rachel for my wife," promised Jacob.

So Jacob worked hard for his Uncle Laban for seven years. Jacob was with Rachel and could walk with her to the pastures and sit and talk with her upon the hill. The seven years did not seem longer than a few days to him because he loved her so dearly.

At the end of seven years, Jacob went to his Uncle Laban and said: "I have kept my promise. I have worked for you seven years. Now let me have Rachel for my wife."

But Laban wanted to keep Jacob working for him. He pretended to be willing to have Rachel marry Jacob and gave a great feast for the men of his family and all his neighbors. Rachel and her sister Leah and the other women had a party by themselves in the inner room. Because in the East the men and women always have separate parties.

The wedding was over and Jacob lifted up the long, heavy veil which covered his bride from head to feet. He looked into the face of Leah!

"What does this mean?" cried Jacob to Laban. "You promised me that if I worked for you for seven years you would give me Rachel for my wife. And now you have married me to Leah."

"Don't you know," answered Laban, "that in this country the younger sister may not marry before her older sister is married? Work for me seven years more and I will give you Rachel for your wife."

In those days a man often had two wives. Jacob was angry at his uncle for deceiving him but he loved Rachel so much that he was willing to work for Laban seven more years to win her as his wife. He was kind to Leah. Her father had forced her to do this thing and he did not blame her for deceiving him. But he knew that he could never love her as much as he loved Rachel.

The day after Jacob married Rachel he began to work another seven years for her father. Laban was a hard master to please. Jacob often thought of his own home in Canaan. There he was treated as the master of the household. But he knew he must keep his promise to his uncle.

Leah had many sons and one daughter. But for many years Rachel had no children. This made her very unhappy. Then God heard her prayers and sent her a son. She named the boy Joseph.

After seven years Jacob was no longer a stranger working for a master who cheated him. Now Jacob owned many sheep and goats and cows and camels. Jacob knew that his father and mother were still alive and wanted to see him and his wives and children.

"We will go the land of Canaan where I was born," Jacob said to his family. "I want my children to live there. For God has promised to give the land to my children and their children after them."

So Jacob and his two wives and all their children and servants started on the journey. They rode camels and donkeys. Some of the servants walked along the road and drove the sheep and cattle before them.

At last Jacob and those who were with him crossed the Jordan River. Soon Jacob would be at home.

But Rachel suddenly grew very ill.

"Let us make a camp here," said Jacob.

Rachel bore a second son and then she died.

Jacob buried his dear wife near the road that leads to Bethlehem. He named the little baby she had left him Benjamin. Jacob carried the child in his arms for the rest of the journey. When he reached home he put the baby in Rebecca's arms. She kissed and blessed the boy and promised to be a mother to him.

The Boy Who Had Strange Dreams

SOMETIMES the Jewish people are called the Children of Israel. That is because the Jewish families of today came from the families of Jacob's twelve sons. And Jacob is sometimes called Israel.

Jacob loved all his sons who became the fathers of the twelve tribes, or families, of Israel. Because he loved Rachel so much he loved best the two sons she had left him, Joseph and Benjamin. Benjamin was still a little fellow living in his grandmother's tent. But Joseph was a big, strong boy who liked to give orders to the servants and even to his older brothers.

Joseph was his father's favorite. His older brothers

worked hard every day. They sowed and reaped the grain in the fields: they took the flocks to pasture. Joseph never did any work. His older brothers dressed like shepherds; Joseph had a bright new robe for every day of the week. On his birthday his father gave him a coat of many colors, red, blue and yellow and brown; the belt was made of many colored wools twisted together.

The boy was very proud of his new coat and wore it every day although his father told him he ought to keep it for feast days. But his brothers were very angry. They said to each other: "Lazy Joseph goes about dressed like a prince. We are dressed like our father's servants."

The brothers hated Joseph more than ever when one morning he told them a dream he had had the night before.

Joseph said: "This is the dream I dreamed last night. I dreamed we were binding sheaves of grain in our father's field. My sheaf arose and stood upright. And the eleven other sheaves bowed down to it just as a king's servants bow down to him."

"Do you dare to tell us that you are like a king and we ought to bow down to you?" asked his brothers. They were very angry.

A few days later at breakfast Joseph began: "I have dreamed another strange dream. Last night I dreamed the sun and the moon and eleven stars bowed down to me."

This time even his father was angry at Joseph. "You talk as though you were the ruler of this household," he said. "Why should you dream that I and your brothers bowed down to you?" He said nothing more but he often remembered Joseph's strange dream. Could it really mean that some day the eleven strong and proud sons of Israel would bow down to their younger brother?

One evening Jacob's sons did not return from the pasture with their sheep. Jacob was frightened, "Perhaps," he said, "some of the young lambs have gone astray and my sons are looking for them. Or some of our wild neighbors have tried to steal sheep from our flocks and my sons are fighting them."

When they had not returned the next morning, Jacob called Joseph to him.

"My son," said Jacob, "take off that fine coat of many colors which you are wearing and put on a plain shepherd's robe. I do not want you to soil your fine robe with the dust of the road or tear it upon some thorn bush. Now hurry and go out to the pasture and see whether all is well with your brothers and with the sheep. Then hurry home and tell me how they are."

Joseph was proud of his coat of many colors. He

disobeyed his father and wore it when he went out to look for his brothers. He found them in a distant pasture. It was noonday and they were resting in the shadow of some high rocks. They saw him from far off.

"The dreamer is coming," growled Judah. "Get ready to bow down to him."

"He is wearing his coat of many colors," said Levi. "He has nothing to do but dress like a peacock and walk down here to spy on us."

"Let us kill him," Simeon said to his brothers. "We will kill him and throw his body into one of the pits in the ground. We can tell our father that a wild animal has killed him."

"Yes," said Levi, "let us kill him. Then we shall see what will become of his dreams."

"No, no!" said Reuben. He hated Joseph as much as the others did, but he was not wicked enough to want to kill his brother. "Do not shed his blood. Just throw him into the pit and he will soon die from hunger and thirst." He said this to deceive his brothers. He knew he was not strong enough to take Joseph away from them if they really meant to kill him. But he said to himself: "If they leave him in a pit, when they are gone I will draw him out again. Then I can take him back to my father."

Now Joseph came up to where his brothers were resting in the shade of the great rocks. "Our father says—"

he began. But they laughed at him and would not listen. All of the angry brothers except Reuben jumped upon young Joseph. They tore off his new coat of many colors. They bound him with ropes and threw him into a deep pit.

"Look!" said Simeon and he pointed toward the road which led to faraway Egypt. The brothers turned to look. They saw a caravan of Ishmaelites. The men of the desert rode their camels proudly. Every camel was heaped high with bags of spices to sell in Egypt.

"They are Ishmaelites," said Judah. "They are merchants on their way to Egypt. Why should we kill our brother? If we sell him to the Ishmaelites they will give us a good price for him."

"Yes, let us sell him to the Ishmaelites," cried several of the brothers.

Judah ran to the road. He stood at the roadside waving Joseph's bright coat of many colors. "Stop, O Ishmaelites!" called Judah at the top of his voice.

The leader of the Ishmaelites stopped his camel. The other merchants stopped also.

"What do you want with us?" he asked.

"We have a slave to sell to you," said Judah. He nodded to Levi and Simeon, who ran to draw Joseph out of the pit. He was very badly frightened and almost sick from crying.

"He is very handsome and strong," said Judah to the

leader of the Ishmaelites. "You can get a good price for him if you sell him for a slave in Egypt."

"How much do you want for him?" asked the merchant.

"Fifty pieces of silver," answered Judah.

"I will give you ten," said the merchant.

Judah was in a hurry to have them take Joseph away. He did not want to bargain any longer. "Give me twenty pieces of silver in my hand and he is yours," said Judah.

The leader of the Ishmaelites leaned down from his camel and counted twenty pieces of silver into Judah's hand. One of the camels had no rider. Several of the merchants lifted Joseph upon its back and tied him tightly to the saddle bags that he could not fall off. The leader hit his camel and the animal began to move slowly down the road; the other camels followed him. Joseph's brothers could hear him crying until he was out of sight.

"What will we tell our father?" asked Simeon. He looked frightened. He was already sorry that he had sold his own brother for a slave.

"Let us kill a goat from the flock," said Judah. "We will dip Joseph's coat of many colors in the goat's blood. Then we will take it to our father and show it to him. He will believe us when we tell him that some wild beast has killed our brother."

Joseph's brothers killed a goat from the flock. They dipped the torn coat in the goat's blood. They brought the coat of many colors to Jacob.

When the brothers returned home that evening, Jacob's first question was: "Where is your brother Joseph?"

The brothers showed Jacob the torn bloody coat. "This we have found," they said.

For many days Jacob sat upon the ground. He mourned for his favorite son, Joseph, and nobody could comfort him. For Jacob could not know that Joseph was safe and alive in Egypt.

From a Prison to a Throne

AT first young Joseph had a very hard time in Egypt. It is never easy to be a slave. It was very hard for Joseph. He had never worked in his whole life; he had always had his way. The Ishmaelites sold him to a rich nobleman in the land of Egypt. Soon the nobleman was angry with Joseph. He sent Joseph to prison.

It was harder to be in prison than to be a slave in the rich nobleman's house. Joseph had little to eat and drink. He could not tell the day from the night. For he was kept in a dark cell underground. At first he was very lonely. He never saw anyone but the keeper of the prison. This man brought him food and drink every day but did not speak to him.

Joseph was very glad when two Egyptians were sent to live with him in his cell. One was the chief of the butlers of the King of Egypt and had always poured the king's wine. The other was the chief of the king's bakers. The Pharaoh, as the king of Egypt was called, was angry with them. They did not know how long they would have to stay in prison.

One morning they said to Joseph: "We have both had such strange dreams. We wonder what they can mean."

"Tell me your dreams," said Joseph. "I am not very wise but perhaps the God of my father Jacob will tell me what to say to you."

"In my dream," began the chief butler, "I saw a vine with three branches. The vine budded. Then I saw ripe grapes growing upon it. Pharaoh's cup was in my hand. I took the grapes and squeezed them into Pharaoh's royal cup. Then I put the cup into Pharaoh's hand. Can you tell me the meaning of my dream?"

Joseph thought a moment. Then he told the chief butler: "This is the meaning of your dream. The three branches of the vine mean three days. In three days Pharaoh will take you out of prison. You will be his chief butler again and put his royal cup of wine into his hand."

"Thank you," answered the chief butler. "I hope you

have given me the true meaning of my dream. I hope I shall soon be free."

"When you are free," answered Joseph, "I hope you will not forget me. I hope you will beg Pharaoh to take me out of this prison."

Then the chief baker told Joseph his dream. He said: "I dreamed that I carried three baskets of fine white bread on my head. In the top basket there were many kinds of food I had baked for Pharaoh. And birds came and ate the food out of the basket on my head."

Joseph thought a moment. Then he told the chief baker: "This is the meaning of your dream. The three baskets are three days. Before three days are over, Pharaoh will order the keeper of the prison to cut off your head. The keeper of the prison will hang your body upon a tree and the birds of the air will peck at it."

The chief baker tried to pretend that Joseph had not told him the real meaning of his dream. But at the end of the third day the keeper of the prison came to the dark cell. He told the chief baker that he must die. But he told the chief butler that Pharaoh had sent orders to set him free. Again the chief butler thanked Joseph for telling him the meaning of his dream. The chief butler promised to remember Joseph and to ask Pharaoh to set him free.

But the chief butler forgot his promise. He did not

tell Pharaoh about Joseph. For two long years Joseph sat lonely and homesick in his prison cell. How he missed his kind father and his little brother Benjamin. He even missed his wicked brothers who had sold him as a slave. He said to himself: "I was often bad to them. I used to spy upon my brothers and tell my father tales to get them into trouble. I used to pretend that I was king and they were my servants. Now I am a slave. I may have to stay in this prison for the rest of my life and never look upon my father's face again."

Then one night Pharaoh, the ruler over Egypt, had a strange dream. In the morning he called the wise men of his house to come before him and tell him the meaning of his strange dream. The wise men thought and thought. But they could not tell Pharaoh the meaning of his dream.

The chief butler, who had been in prison, stood beside Pharaoh to serve him his breakfast. But Pharaoh was too worried to eat or drink. He pushed his beautiful silver cup away. Then the chief butler remembered Joseph.

"O Pharaoh," he said, "I know a man who will tell you the true meaning of your dream."

Then he told Pharaoh how he had met Joseph in prison and how Joseph had told him the true meaning of his strange dream.

Pharaoh sent for Joseph to come before him at once.

The keeper of the prison helped Joseph bathe and shaved him and cut his long tangled hair. He put a plain clean robe on Joseph and led him before Pharaoh. Joseph bowed so low that his forehead almost touched the ground. He was afraid because he did not know why the ruler over Egypt had sent for him.

"Listen well," said Pharaoh to Joseph, "while I tell you the dream that I have dreamed. I dreamed last night that I stood by the river. And out of the river came seven cows. They were sleek and fat and they ate the reed grasses that grew along the river. Then seven other cows came out of the river. They were ugly and very thin. These cows stood by the river. Then they ate the seven cows which were sleek and fat.

"This was the dream I dreamed last night," said Pharaoh. "And I dreamed also that I saw seven ears of grain growing upon one stalk. The ears of grain were full and good. Then I saw a stalk growing with seven ears upon it. They were withered and thin and the east wind blew upon them until they dried up before my eyes. But first the seven thin ears of grain swallowed up the seven ears which were full and good. Now tell me if you can the meaning of my dream."

Joseph answered Pharaoh and said: "It is not I but God who tells you the meaning of your two dreams. The seven fat cows are seven good years, when there will be plenty to eat in the land of Egypt. The seven lean cows are the seven years which will follow. There will not be enough to eat in the land of Egypt and everyone will be lean and hungry. The seven full ears of grain are also for the seven years of plenty. The seven withered ears are for the seven years of hunger when the east wind will dry up all the grain in the land."

"If that is the true meaning of my dreams," said Pharaoh, "what does your God tell me to do to save the people of Egypt from hunger?"

"Let Pharaoh find a wise man he can trust," answered Joseph. "Let this man send servants all over the land of Egypt in the years when there is plenty to eat. These servants must gather one-fifth of all the grain in the fields. Let this grain be kept in Pharaoh's storehouses. When the seven lean years come the food in the store houses will feed all the people."

Pharaoh thought long over what Joseph had said. He gave Joseph his royal silver cup for telling him the true meaning of his dreams. He gave Joseph robes of fine linen and put a gold chain about his neck. Then Pharaoh took off his signet ring; he always used it to sign his royal orders and no other man in Egypt had used it before. Now Pharaoh gave his signet ring to Joseph and told him to sign any orders he might want to send to the people of Egypt. For Joseph was the second man in Egypt now and only Pharaoh was mightier than he. Joseph rode in a chariot made of fine woods and gold and silver. When the greatest men of all Egypt came to talk to him they bowed to the ground. Joseph received them as he sat in a great carved chair of ebony and ivory; it was placed just a little lower than the throne of Pharaoh himself.

When Joseph was a foolish young boy in his father's house, he had been proud of his fine clothes and his father's gifts. But now he was not proud.

"I wonder why men praise me for my wisdom," Joseph often said to himself. "It was not my own strength and wisdom that made me ruler over Egypt. It was the God of Jacob, my father, Who lifted me from a prison to a throne."

Joseph and His Brothers

JOSEPH had gathered enough grain in the good years to feed the people of Egypt when the famine began. Everybody in Egypt had enough to eat. But in the land of Canaan many people were hungry.

Jacob heard there was plenty of grain in Egypt. He said to his sons: "Go to Egypt. Buy all the grain you can get there. Bring it back quickly that we may eat and live and not die."

"May I go with my brothers?" asked young Benjamin who stood beside his father's chair.

"No," said Jacob. "Since your brother, Joseph, was taken from me, you are the dearest thing I have on earth." Old Jacob wept when he spoke Joseph's name. For many years he had been sure Joseph was dead; but he never could cease from mourning over his loss.

So Jacob's ten sons took their donkeys and their packs of food and drink and set out for Egypt. Each man carried a big empty sack. They hoped to bring back enough grain to last for many weeks.

Joseph knew his brothers at once when they came before him and asked to buy grain. It was many years since he had last seen them, but they had hardly changed. But Joseph was no longer a frightened young boy in a coat of many colors. He was a grown, bearded man. He wore rich robes and Pharaoh's golden chain hung about his neck. His brothers did not recognize him.

They bowed before him just as Joseph had dreamed long ago.

"Where do you come from? What do you want in Egypt?" asked Joseph. He pretended to speak roughly.

"We come from the land of Canaan," answered Joseph's brothers. "We want to buy grain."

Joseph pretended to be angry. "That is not why you have come," he told his brothers. "I believe you are spies. You have all come together to do some evil thing against Pharaoh."

"No, my lord," answered Judah. "We have come together because we are brothers. Our father, Jacob, had twelve sons."

"There are ten of you before me," said Joseph. "Where are the other sons of your father's house?"

"One of our brothers is dead," Judah told him. "The youngest, Benjamin, is with our father. Our father was afraid to have Benjamin come with us."

Joseph wanted to see his little brother, Benjamin, again. He said: "If you are honest men you have nothing to fear from Pharaoh or from me. I want to see your youngest brother. Do not dare to come before me again unless you bring him with you. Now go and carry home the food you have bought from me. But as a promise that you will return, one of you must stay here in prison."

The brothers were frightened. They said to each other: "He is treating us like wicked men. We meant no harm when we came to Egypt. But we did a cruel and wicked thing when we sold our brother, Joseph. Now one of us will be treated like a slave."

Joseph commanded that the men from Canaan should leave Simeon as a promise that they would return with Benjamin. He ordered his servants to fill their bags with grain. He also told his servants to put in every man's sack the money he had paid for the grain.

On the way back to Canaan, the brothers stopped by the road to eat. Levi opened his sack first; he wanted to give his donkey a little grain for its supper. There on the top of the grain lay the pieces of money he had given Joseph. "See what I found in my sack!" he cried.

The others tore open their sacks. In every one of the sacks lay the money which had been paid for the grain. The brothers looked at each other and they were afraid. They said: "Who is this man who rules over Egypt and is second only to Pharaoh himself? Why did he not keep the money we paid him?"

Wondering and afraid, the brothers returned to their father's house in Canaan. They told old Jacob all that had happened to them in Egypt. And they said: "We dare not return to Egypt for more grain unless we bring Benjamin with us. For so has the ruler of Egypt commanded us."

Jacob began to cry. "God took Joseph away from me," he said. "And now Simeon is in prison in the land of Egypt. Will you take my youngest, Benjamin, away from me also?"

Soon the grain brought from Egypt was all eaten. Then Jacob called his sons to him and said: "Go again to Egypt and buy us a little food."

"Father," said Judah, "we dare not go before the ruler of Egypt again unless we have Benjamin with us."

"I dare not let him go," answered old Jacob. "If he goes with you I may never see him again."

"Father," said Judah, "if we do not go to Egypt for

grain, all of our family will starve. And we dare not go to Egypt without Benjamin. I promise you that I will do my best to take care of him and bring him safely back to you."

So Jacob allowed his best-loved Benjamin to go with his brothers to Egypt. And Jacob sent presents to the ruler of Egypt, the finest fruits of the land and spices and honey and nuts. He also gave each of his sons twice the money he thought the grain might cost. He said: "It was surely a mistake that you found the money in your sacks. Now pay it back when you buy more grain. May God take care of all you. May He also send Benjamin back with you when you return to Canaan."

At last the brothers stood before Joseph. They bowed low and gave him the presents their father had sent him.

Joseph looked at Benjamin. Little Benjamin stood next to his brother Judah. He held Judah's hand. Joseph could remember his mother a little. It seemed to him that he saw her face again. For Benjamin looked like his beautiful dead mother.

"May God bless you, my son," Joseph said to Benjamin. Joseph was afraid they would see his tears. He went into an inner room; he wept to see his little brother. For he had thought he would never see Benjamin again.

Then Joseph went back to his brothers. He ordered the servants to place food before them and sent for

Simeon to eat with the others. He told the servants to give Benjamin five times as much food as the others. So they drank and were merry.

Then Joseph called his chief servant to him and said: "Fill every man's sack with grain and put in the sack the money he has paid. Into the sack of the youngest put the grain and the money and this cup. It is the royal silver cup which I had from the hand of Pharaoh."

The next morning Joseph's brothers gathered in the courtyard. They tied the heavy bags of grain on their donkeys; they climbed upon their donkeys and rode away.

But Joseph sent his chief servant after them and the man said just what Joseph had told him to say. The servant said: "My master says that one of you has carried away his silver cup."

The brothers were surprised at his words and answered him. "Why should we steal anything from your master?" they said. "Didn't we return the money which did not belong to us?"

But the chief servant would not listen. He took them all back to the palace.

"Why did you steal my silver cup?" asked Joseph. "Why did one of you hide in his sack the royal cup I had from Pharaoh's own hand?"

"My lord," answered Judah, "we have stolen neither silver nor gold from your house. Search our sacks and see for yourself. If you find your lost cup in the sack of any of Jacob's sons, you may make him your slave forever. And the rest of us will be your slaves also."

Then Joseph told them to empty their sacks upon the ground before him. Every man emptied the grain upon the ground, one after the other. Benjamin's turn came last. The boy was very frightened. His hands trembled so that Levi had to help him. There on the floor in the middle of the grain lay the shining silver cup!

"My lord," cried Judah, falling upon the ground before Joseph, "I do not know how the cup found its way into this boy's sack. But I know he did not steal it. Do not punish him. When I left home I promised our father that I would not let any harm come to the boy. So punish me instead. I will be your slave for the rest of my days. But let Benjamin return in peace to our father's house."

The other brothers began to cry. They fell upon the ground and begged Joseph not to punish Benjamin. They said they would be willing to be Joseph's slaves forever if he would only let Benjamin return to his father's house. Judah wept when he said that old Jacob still mourned for a young son he had lost years ago. He said Jacob would surely die if Benjamin did not come back to him.

Then Joseph knew that his brothers were no longer cruel and wicked. They were willing to live as slaves the rest of their lives if they could save their father pain. He drew the weeping Benjamin toward him and kissed him.

"Come nearer to me," he said to his frightened older brothers. "Look into my face. Don't you know me, Judah? Don't you remember, Reuben, how you begged the others not to kill me?"

The brothers looked at each other. They were afraid to speak.

"Do not be afraid," Joseph told them. "You were cruel to me and tried to harm me. But the God of Jacob turned all the evil you did into good. For I became a ruler in Egypt and have fed the hungry. Now go back to my father and give to him the gifts I will send with you. Tell him I am alive and well in Egypt. Tell him I must stay here for I am a ruler in the land. But he must come back with you and live in my house for the rest of his days."

The brothers returned to Canaan. Joseph had given them all rich gifts and he sent gifts of great price to his father. At first Jacob could not believe the good news. Then he said: "Joseph, my son, is yet alive. I will go and see him before I die."

Moses in the Bulrushes

JACOB, who was sometimes called Israel, came down to Egypt to see his son, Joseph. He brought with him his eleven sons and their wives and children. The servants of Jacob's household also came with him, and he took all his sheep and cattle. Joseph was a mighty ruler in Egypt. He gave his brothers lands. The Children of Israel were shepherds in Egypt just as they had been in the land of Canaan.

For many years the Children of Israel and their children lived in peace in Egypt. Then Joseph died and Pharaoh, his master and friend, died also. A new Pharaoh ruled over Egypt. This Pharaoh was not a friend of Joseph. He hated the Children of Israel and made them his slaves. He gave orders that they should work in his brickyards every day from early morning until dark.

Pharaoh knew that there were many of Jacob's grandchildren and their children living in Egypt. He was afraid of them. He said: "Let the girl children grow up. They will make good slaves. But the boy children may become strong fighters and make war against me. I will give orders that every boy child shall be killed as soon as he is born."

Jochebed was a woman of the family of Levi. She had two children, a son named Aaron and a daughter named Miriam. When her second son was born she did not know what to do. She kept the child hidden in her little house for three months. Every day she was sure that Pharaoh's soldiers would find the baby. She knew that the soldiers would surely kill her for not obeying Pharaoh. She was not afraid for herself. But she did not want any harm to come to her child.

So Jochebed made a little basket of twisted bulrushes she had picked on the bank of the river. She rubbed pitch upon the basket that no water could come into it. Then she lined the basket with a soft cloth and put the baby into its new bed. Jochebed and her daughter, Miriam, went down to the river very early in the morning before anybody was around to see them. Jochebed put the basket in a clump of bulrushes on the bank of the river. She told her daughter Miriam to hide behind a tree to see what happened. Then Jochebed went back to her house. She prayed to God to take care of her little child.

Pharaoh's daughter, the princess of Egypt, came down to the river to bathe. She was a tall, beautiful woman; her eyes were always sad. She was unhappy because she did not have a child to care for and love. Miriam watched the princess walk down to the river bank. Four of her handmaidens were with her; two walked before her and two came after her. One of the handmaidens took off the bright blue cloak the princess wore over her long white robe. One of the girls knelt to untie the lovely lady's sandals.

The princess saw something white in the middle of the clump of bulrushes on the bank of the river. "Go and see what is fluttering in the wind over there," she said to one of the handmaidens.

The girl ran to the place where the basket was hidden. She brought the basket back to the princess.

The princess lifted the white cloth she had seen fluttering in the wind. She saw the little baby lying in the basket. The baby began to cry and the princess rocked it gently in her arms. She pitied the child and loved it for she loved little children.

"This is one of the poor babies my father Pharaoh

has ordered to be thrown into the river," the princess said to her handmaidens. She took the child out of the basket and held it close. "Do not cry, baby," she said to the child. "I will not let anybody hurt you."

Miriam came out from behind the tree. She bowed low before the princess. Miriam said: "Shall I bring you a nurse to take care of the child?"

"Yes," answered the princess.

Miriam ran as fast as she could to the little house where her mother waited. She brought Jochebed back with her. Jochebed bowed low before the princess. The daughter of Pharaoh placed the baby in her arms.

"Take this child home with you," said the princess of Egypt. "Nurse him for me and give him the best of care. When the child is old enough to do without your care, bring him to the palace. There I will bring him up as my own son."

"What will you name the child?" asked one of the handmaidens.

"I will call him Moses," answered the princess. "Because the name means drawn out of the water, and I have saved him from the river today."

The Prince Who Became a Shepherd

WHEN Moses was four years old his mother brought him to Pharaoh's daughter. The princess treated him like her own son. She gave him beautiful robes to wear and beautiful toys to play with. Moses ate at her table from dishes of gold; he drank from a silver cup. Everyone bowed down before him for he was a prince in Egypt.

Moses grew up in the palace. The Children of Israel were all slaves to Pharaoh. They worked in the brickyards from early morning until dark. But the brickyards were a long way from the palace. Moses could not hear the crying of his people.

One day Moses took a long, long walk. He had never walked so far from the palace before. He passed the brickyards and stopped to watch the men and women who were working under the hot sun. The Egyptian taskmasters walked up and down and watched the workers. These taskmasters carried big whips. Whenever a man stopped working for a moment, the nearest taskmaster hit him with the whip until he went on working.

Moses walked to the end of the brickyard. He saw a very old man lying on the ground. Moses walked over to him.

"What is the matter, old man?" he asked.

The old man raised his head. "I am too old to work," he said. "And today I am sick from the hot sun. So I crept over here to rest a little. I hope the cruel taskmaster will not find me."

At that moment one of the taskmasters came across the brickyard. He saw the old man upon the ground. "Get up and go to work, you lazy old man!" cried the taskmaster.

The old man tried to stand. But he fell to the ground. The taskmaster rushed to his side. He raised his heavy whip and hit the old man again and again.

"Stop!" cried Moses.

The taskmaster did not seem to hear Moses. He hit the old man again.

Moses was afraid the taskmaster would kill the old man. Moses snatched the whip from the taskmaster's hand. He hit the taskmaster on the head with it. Moses did not mean to kill the taskmaster. But the taskmaster dropped to the ground. He did not move again. He was dead.

Moses covered the dead taskmaster with sand. Now what should he do? He thought the princess might forgive him if she heard what he had done. But Pharaoh would surely punish him. Moses knew he must go away and hide for a while.

So Moses pulled his robe up to his knees that he could walk easier. He drew his headcloth around his face that no one would recognize him on the road. All that day he walked as fast as he could. For seven days he journeyed until he reached the land of Midian.

"Perhaps I can live here in peace," Moses said to himself. "I am sure that Pharaoh's soldiers will never look for me here."

Moses found a well of clear, cold water. He drew up the bucket and drank until he was satisfied; he poured the water over his hands and hot, tired feet.

As Moses rested under a nearby tree he saw seven girls coming up the path. They drove their sheep before them. The girls drew water from the well and poured it into the trough for their sheep to drink. But two shepherds with their flocks came up at that moment.

The shepherds brought their own sheep to the watering trough.

The girls were frightened and did not seem to know what to do. Moses ran over to the well. Moses was very tall and strong. When the shepherds saw him they drew back.

"Drive off your sheep!" Moses told the two shepherds. The frightened men obeyed. The girls watered their sheep and turned to go home. The oldest girl turned to speak to Moses.

"Thank you, stranger, for helping us," she said. "If you come home with me I know my father will welcome you and give you food and a place to sleep. He will want to thank you for helping his daughters."

"What is your name?" asked Moses, as they walked together.

"Zipporah," she answered. "What is yours and from what land have you come?"

"I have come from Egypt and my name is Moses," he answered. But he did not tell her he had been a prince in Egypt.

Zipporah's father welcomed Moses. He asked Moses to stay in his house. Moses soon knew that he loved Zipporah. She loved him also and was very happy when her father gave her to Moses as his wife.

Zipporah's father had no sons to help him. That is why his daughters had always taken the sheep to the pasture and to the well. But now Moses took care of the flocks. Instead of the rich robes the princess had given him, Moses now wore the plain coarse robe which Zipporah wove for him. Instead of royal food on golden plates he ate cheese from a clay bowl. Instead of living in a palace with servants to wait on him, he worked hard from morning until evening.

But Moses, who had been a prince in Egypt, was glad to be a shepherd in the land of Midian. He loved Zipporah and his children. He liked to take the sheep out to the pasture. He was happy in Midian and was sure that he would never want to go back to Egypt.

The Burning Bush

ONE day Moses led his flock to a new pasture. The
pasture was a long, long way from home. Moses
sat down to rest on a low flat stone.

Moses looked at a thorn bush that grew nearby. It
was a low bush growing in the pasture. Suddenly the
bush seemed to be on fire. The flames sprang high into
the air. They died down; again the flames rose and this
time they rose higher than before.

The shepherd thought he was dreaming. A moment
before the bush before him had been like any thorn
bush in the pasture. Now it blazed like a great fire.
Moses walked over to the thorn bush to look at it. He

73

was careful not to go too near; he feared he might burn his robe. Yes, the bush was surely on fire. It seemed very strange to Moses that although he stood watching for a long time, the fire did not burn up the little thorn bush.

Suddenly a voice spoke to Moses. It came from the burning bush and it called his name. "Moses, Moses!" said the voice.

Moses was almost afraid to speak. He was sure the voice was the voice of God. At last he said: "Here am I." He waited for the voice to go on.

"I am the God of your fathers, the God of Abraham, the God of Isaac, and the God of Jacob," said the voice.

Moses fell upon his knees and hid his face in his cloak.

God said to Moses: "I have seen the great trouble of My people, the Children of Israel. The Egyptians are very cruel to them. My people cry out to Me to save them from their taskmasters. I will save them from their taskmasters. I will bring them to a good land, a land flowing with milk and honey. They will be free there and have plenty to eat. I will send you back to Egypt. You will go before Pharaoh and tell him to set the Children of Israel free."

Moses was so frightened that he could hardly answer God. At last he said: "I am not the man to go before Pharaoh. I am not wise enough or good enough to bring the Children of Israel out of Egypt."

"Do not be afraid," God told Moses. "I will be with you. You shall say to the Children of Israel: The God of your fathers, the God of Abraham, of Isaac, and of Jacob appeared to me. He said that He has seen your trouble. He says that He will bring you to a land flowing with milk and honey."

"But," said Moses, "the Children of Israel will not believe me."

"What is that in your hand?" asked God.

Moses held out the stick he carried to push the sheep back into the path when they tried to run away. "I have a rod in my hand," he answered.

"Throw your rod upon the ground," commanded God.

Moses threw the rod upon the ground. It turned into a snake which twisted in the dust.

"Take it by the tail," commanded God.

Moses put out his hand and caught the snake by the tail. The snake grew quiet; it lay still; it was a rod again.

"This will be a sign for all the people," said God. "And I will help you to do many wonders. Everyone will believe your words."

"But," answered Moses, "I will not know how to talk to the Children of Israel. I will not know how to talk to Pharaoh when I stand before him. I am not a good speaker; I have a slow tongue and I never know what to say."

"Your brother Aaron can speak well," answered God. "I will send him to you as soon as you go to Egypt. He will be glad to see you. Your mother is dead but your sister Miriam will tell Aaron how she hid you in the bulrushes by the river. Then Aaron will tell the Children of Israel that you belong to them. I will give you the right words to speak. Then you can tell Aaron what to say. Now take up the rod. You will do many wonders with it in My name."

So Moses took up his rod and drove his sheep before him back to the sheepfold.

The next day he set out for the land of Egypt.

Before the Throne of Pharaoh

GOD told Aaron to go into the wilderness to meet Moses, his brother. Moses told his older brother all that God had said from the burning bush. They went back to Egypt together. Then Aaron called together all the elders of the Children of Israel, the wise men and the leaders, and told them that God had sent Moses to set them free. The people believed and they bowed their heads and thanked God for sending Moses to save them.

Then Moses and Aaron went to Pharaoh, the ruler over all Egypt, and stood before his throne. Aaron spoke out boldly. "Thus says the Lord, the God of

Israel," Aaron told Pharaoh. " 'Let My people go that they may hold a feast in My honor in the wilderness.' " These were the words that God had told Moses his brother Aaron must say.

Pharaoh laughed. He and his people had many, many gods. Pharaoh was sure that his gods were the strongest gods on earth, just as the Egyptians were the strongest people of that day. Pharaoh said to Aaron and Moses: "Who is the Lord Who tells you to hold a feast in the wilderness? I have never heard of Him. I shall not let your lazy people leave their work to hold a feast in the wilderness."

Then Pharaoh said to his taskmasters: "These men have come to the Children of Israel and told them they should go into the wilderness to hold a feast in honor of their God. If you gave the Children of Israel enough work to do in my brickyards they would not have time to think of holidays. Make them work harder than ever and they will stop having such foolish thoughts."

So Pharaoh's taskmasters made the Children of Israel work even harder than before. When they could not do all their work they were cruelly beaten. The Children of Israel blamed Moses and Aaron. They said: "If you had not asked Pharaoh to give us a holiday, this new trouble would not have come upon us."

Moses spoke to God. "We have brought new trouble to our people," he said.

"If Pharaoh will not let the Children of Israel leave Egypt when you come to him in peace," answered God, "he must be punished until he is frightened enough to listen to Me."

God told Moses and Aaron what to do. They went again before Pharaoh. He sat proudly on his throne in the great hall of the palace. Behind his throne stood his wise men who could do magic; on either side of the throne Pharaoh's soldiers stood in straight, tall rows. Every soldier carried a shining shield and spear. But Pharaoh thought that his wise men could protect him better than the soldiers could, because the wise men could work wonders.

Aaron stood before Pharaoh. He took the shepherd's rod from his brother's hand and threw it upon the ground. The rod became a snake twisting upon the marble floor.

"Do you think I am afraid of you because you can do magic?" cried Pharaoh. He turned to his wise men. "Show these foolish men that you are more powerful than they are," he said, "just as I am more powerful than their God."

Every wise man always carried a small rod which he used when he worked wonders before Pharaoh. They all came before the throne and threw their rods upon the ground. The rods turned into snakes which twisted and turned upon the marble floor. But the snake which had been Moses' rod ate up the other snakes one after the other. The wise men were ashamed. But Pharaoh pretended that he was not afraid. He laughed and ordered his soldiers to drive Moses and Aaron away.

But in his heart Pharaoh was afraid of Moses.

The next morning Pharaoh went down to the river to bathe. First his bodyguard walked down the path to the river. The soldiers carried bright shields and spears. Pharaoh followed with his servants. They stopped on the bank of the river. There stood Moses and Aaron waiting for Pharaoh just as God had commanded them to do.

"Must I see those men wherever I go?" cried Pharaoh to the captain of his bodyguard. "Take them to prison."

The soldiers were about to drag Moses and Aaron away when Moses spoke.

"You would not listen before when I told you the words of the Lord," he said. "Now the God of my people will punish you with one trouble after another until you set us free."

Aaron went closer to the river and held out the rod which could make magic. Everyone cried out in fear and wonder, for the water of the river turned to blood. One of Pharaoh's slaves had gone down to the river to the river to fill her pitcher. She ran to Pharaoh; she showed him that the water in the pitcher had turned to blood.

Now Pharaoh was really afraid. He turned and almost ran back to the palace. His servants and the soldiers of his bodyguard followed him as fast as they could. Nobody thought after that about putting Moses and Aaron in prison. All over Egypt people were talking about the trouble or plague which had come to the land. This first plague lasted seven days. The fish in the rivers and ponds died. People who were not rich enough to have wine almost died of thirst.

But this was only the first plague. When Pharaoh still refused to listen to Moses, other plagues came upon the land. The rivers and ponds became full of frogs; the frogs seemed to go everywhere. A women would look into the wooden trough where she had left the bread dough; frogs would jump in her face. When she was ready to bake the bread and opened the oven, a frog would jump out. Pharaoh told all his servants to drive the frogs away but there seemed to be more frogs in the palace than anywhere else. He could not sleep at night because frogs kept hopping all over the bed.

Pharaoh sent for Moses and Aaron. He promised them that if they drove the frogs away he would let the Children of Israel go into the wilderness. But as soon as the frogs stopped troubling him, Pharaoh forgot his promise. So new plagues came upon Egypt, the plague of gnats and the plague of flies, the plague of darkness and the plague of hail. The crops died in the fields. Pharaoh knew that his people would try to harm him if they had to suffer any more. Everytime a plague came, Pharaoh would promise to set the Children of Israel free. But as soon as the plague was over Pharaoh would forget his promise.

So each plague grew harder to bear than the last; the people grew sick and many of them blamed Pharaoh for their sickness. Still he would not let the Children of Israel leave the country.

Then the most cruel punishment of all came to Pharaoh and his people. The Angel of Death passed over every Egyptian home. The first-born son of every family in the land suddenly died, from the oldest son of Pharaoh in the beautiful palace to the first-born of the slaves in their poor little houses. Only the first-born of the Children of Israel were saved and did not die.

It was midnight. In every Egyptian home there was weeping and mourning for the first-born. But in the huts where the Children of Israel lived there was hope and joy. For Pharaoh sent for Moses and Aaron and said to them: "Go, leave the land of Egypt. Call the Children of Israel together and lead them into the wilderness to serve their God."

So the head of every family told his household to get

ready to leave the land of Egypt. Everyone hurried to get away as fast as he could. The women took the dough out of the troughs. They could not wait for it to rise. But they took it with them and the next day put the dough out in the sun to bake. It did not rise and looked like big, flat crackers. These were called *Matzoh*. Every year the Children of Israel eat *Matzoh* for a whole week. On the first night there is a feast called *Seder*. Then the father of the family tells the story of the first Passover to his children.

This holiday is called Passover because it was given the Children of Israel to remember the first Passover when the Angel of Death passed over their houses and spared the first-born.

The Dance by the Sea

MOSES led the Children of Israel out of Egypt. Moses said to the people: "We must travel miles and miles across the wilderness before we come into the Land of Promise. It is a good land flowing with milk and honey. God promised it to Abraham, Isaac and Jacob and to their children forever."

"What if we should lose our way?" cried the people.

"We shall not lose our way," Moses promised them. "God will travel before us. By day we will follow the great mass of clouds that lies just before us. By night God will turn the clouds into fire to show us our path."

As soon as the Children of Israel had started on their

long journey, Pharaoh said: "Why did I let those people go? They were good slaves. I need their work in my brickyards." He called together all his soldiers. Some rode upon horses, some rode in chariots. Pharaoh and his most trusted captains led them, and all rode as fast as they could.

Moses and the Children of Israel had made camp on the shore of the Red Sea. Moses wished them to eat and drink and rest before they really started their long journey.

Suddenly Pharaoh and his captains in their chariots and the horsemen of Egypt came in sight. The people were afraid. They could see the spears of the Egyptians shining in the sun; they could hear the battle cries of the Egyptian soldiers. The Children of Israel cried to Moses: "Have you brought us here to die?"

But Moses said: "Do not be afraid. The Lord will fight for you today."

Then God spoke to Moses. "Moses," God commanded, "lift up your rod and stretch it over the sea. Then the sea will divide and the Children of Israel will cross over it as easily as if they were walking on dry land."

Moses stretched his rod over the Red Sea. A strong wind blew from the east. The waters divided on either side and there was a path of dry land between them. The waters were like a wall on their right hand and on their left. Then Moses led his people to the further shore of the Red Sea. The men and women and little children all got safely across. Not even their shoes were wet as they climbed up the bank.

Just as the Children of Israel reached the further shore, Pharaoh and his soldiers came up to the other side of the Red Sea. They had just seen Moses lead his people across. Now Pharaoh and his army tried to follow them. But the walls of water fell with a rush and roar and every Egyptian was drowned under the waves.

Then Moses and the Children of Israel sang a song of praise and thanksgiving to God for saving them from their enemies. Miriam, the sister of Moses and Aaron, led the women who danced on the shore of the Red Sea. A long, long journey through the wilderness was before them. But now the people were no longer afraid. Their hearts were strong and full of hope as they sang:

I will sing unto the Lord . . .
The horse and his rider hath He thrown into the sea.
Who is like unto Thee, O Lord, among the mighty?
Who is like unto Thee, glorious in holiness?
The Lord shall reign for ever and ever.

The Beginning of the Long Long Journey

NOW Moses and the Children of Israel were in the wilderness which stretched between Egypt and the Promised Land. As far as they could see there was nothing but sand with a few rocks here and there against the sky. Or, miles and miles apart, there would be a well with a few tall palm trees around it.

For three days the Children of Israel traveled in the wilderness under the hot burning sun. They had no water but what they had brought with them and soon that was all gone. Then they found a well, but the water in it was bitter and no one could drink it.

The people cried out to Moses: "It would have been

better for us to have stayed in Egypt. We were slaves there but we did not die of thirst."

Moses was patient with the people. He prayed to God to help him and God told him to pick up a broken palm tree which lay upon the ground. God told Moses to throw the tree into the water. Now the water was sweet again. The Children of Israel drank the water and filled their pitchers at the well.

Soon all the food they had brought with them from Egypt was eaten. The little children cried for food. Their mothers and their fathers said to Moses: "It would have been better for us to have stayed in Egypt. We had little to eat but bread. But here our children will starve before our eyes."

Then God said to Moses: "I will give this people food. They shall have meat to eat in the evening and bread to eat in the morning."

That very evening the sky grew dark over the camp. At first the Children of Israel thought that a black cloud was crossing the sky. Then they saw that God had sent quails to feed them. The birds lighted upon the ground. They were easy to catch and every man caught enough to feed his family and himself. They made fires and roasted the birds for their suppers.

The next morning when they woke up the Children of Israel thought that the sand was covered with frost.

Everyone asked: "What is this thing? Can this be the bread that God has promised us?"

Moses told the people that this was *manna* which God had sent down from heaven to feed them. The people gathered the *manna*. It tasted very good, like thin bread made with honey. This was the food the Children of Israel ate while they were in the wilderness.

The Children of Israel Receive the Ten Commandments

THIS is the story of the most wonderful thing that ever happened to the Children of Israel. It is the story of the giving of the Ten Commandments.

The Children of Israel reached the wilderness of Sinai. The mountain of Sinai rose dark and tall against the sky. The Children of Israel made their camp at the foot of the mountain. They put up their tents of black goatskin. The flocks of sheep, the goats and the cattle wandered over the rocky ground and ate the coarse brown grass and thistles.

God said to Moses: "I have taken the Children of

Israel out of Egypt where they were slaves. Now they are in the wilderness. But some day they will be a free people in a free land. Pharaoh will not rule over them there. I will be their king. They must have laws that they may live a good life. Come up to the top of the mountain and I will give you the commandments for My people."

Moses told the Children of Israel that God had told him to go up into the mountain of Sinai. He told his brother Aaron to take charge of the camp. Then he took a staff in his hand and began to climb the mountain.

When Moses reached the top of Sinai the mountain seemed to burst into flames of fire. The earth shook; there was lightning and thunder. The Children of Israel in their camp at the foot of the mountain were afraid. But Moses was not afraid. He knew that God would take care of him.

God told Moses to take two pieces of stone and write upon them the commandments for the Children of Israel. And Moses carved the words of God upon the two tablets of stone.

In the camp at the foot of Sinai the people began to be restless. They did not know what had happened to Moses up in the mountains. They were afraid. Many of them could not believe in a God they could not see.

When the Children of Israel lived in Egypt they learned about the Egyptian gods. The Egyptians made statues of their gods out of stone and wood, and sometimes of silver and gold. They said, "These gods will take care of us."

Now the Children of Israel wanted a god they could see. They said to Aaron: "We do not know what has become of Moses. Perhaps he will never come down from the mountain. We will not have anybody to lead us. So we need a strong god to take care of us. Make us a god like the gods of Egypt."

Aaron did not want to do this. He thought the people would not want to give up their gold, so he said: "If you will give me enough gold, I will make you a god like the gods of Egypt."

In those days the men as well as the women wore earrings. The men took the gold earrings from their ears and asked their wives and their sons and their daughters for their gold earrings. They took all the gold earrings to Aaron and said: "Now make us a god like the gods of Egypt."

Aaron melted the gold and made it into the statue of a calf. He put it upon a high stone in the middle of the camp. The people forgot what Moses had told them about God. They clapped their hands with joy. They danced around the Golden Calf and sang: "This is the god which brought us out of the land of Egypt."

Moses came down from the mountain. He carried the tablets of stone on which he had cut the commandments of God. He heard a great shouting in the camp.

"What has happened?" Moses asked himself.

Moses reached a turn in the mountain path from where he could look down into the camp. He saw the statue of the golden calf gleaming in the sunlight. He saw the men and women and children dancing wildly around it. He could hear them singing: "This is the god which brought us out of the land of Egypt."

He was very angry. How could the people forget all that their God had done for them? How could they thank and praise a thing they had made with their own hands? At that moment Moses felt the Children of Israel did not deserve the laws which God had sent them to make them a strong nation. He threw down the tablets so hard that they broke into a hundred pieces on the rocks below.

Then Moses went down into the camp. He looked so angry that the people ran away and hid in their tents. Moses pulled down the Golden Calf and threw it into the fire. He called the people before him and told them they had sinned a great sin. He said: "Surely God will punish you for turning against Him. But I will ask God to forgive you and show you mercy."

Moses said to God: "This people have sinned a great sin and have made them a god of gold. Forgive their sin. Or, if they must be punished, punish me in their place for they are my people and I love them."

"The people have sinned and must be punished," answered God. "But I will still give them My commandments that they may live a good life. Come up into the mountain again and I will have you set My words down upon tablets of stone."

So Moses went up the mountain of Sinai for the second time. Again God told him what to put down upon the two tablets and Moses carved the words on the stones. Then Moses came down from the mountain and read the commandments of God to the people. The men and the women and even the little children promised to obey God's commandments. They said: "All that the Lord has spoken we will do."

These commandments told the Children of Israel that they must always obey and love God because He had taken them out of Egypt. They must not make any statues of Him as the Egyptians tried to do. They should speak His Name only as a holy word and keep His Sabbath as a holy day. These were to be their duties to God.

The Children of Israel were also to have certain duties toward each other and their neighbors. They were to honor their fathers and their mothers; they were not to kill or rob anyone. They must never say anything untrue of their neighbors.

Moses brought these Ten Commandments to the Children of Israel. Little by little they became the laws of the people of the whole world and helped them to be good and happy. That was what God meant when He promised Abraham and Isaac and Jacob that the nations of the earth would be blessed through the Children of Israel.

Moses Leaves His People

GOD had promised the Children of Israel that the land of Canaan would belong to them forever. Now He said to Moses: "Send men out to look over the land of Canaan that they may tell you what they find there. Send a man from every one of the twelve tribes of Israel and let him be a leader among his people."

Moses chose twelve strong brave men to go into Canaan as spies. The strongest and bravest of them were Joshua and Caleb. Moses said to the spies: "See whether the people who live in the land of Canaan are weak or strong; see whether many people live there or only a few. See what kind of cities they live in and whether it would be hard to take these cities in war. Find out for me whether there are plenty of forests and what kind of crops the farmers have. If you can, bring me back some of the fruit of the land. Your lives will be in danger if you fall into the hands of the people of Canaan. But trust in God and be of good courage."

Then the twelve spies said goodby to their families. They took packs of food and flasks of water for their journey. Each man carried a staff in his hand to help him climb the mountains and in his belt each man wore a knife to protect himself. Moses blessed them and they set out for the strange, new land of Canaan.

Weeks passed and the spies did not return. Their families wept and said: "Surely the men Moses sent to spy out Canaan have died there. Wild beasts have killed them. Or the men of Canaan have caught them and put them to death." Then the people blamed Moses for sending out the spies.

But on the fortieth day the spies returned to the camp the Children of Israel had set up in the wilderness. Their shoes were torn by the rocks; their clothes were in rags. But the men were strong and well after their hard journey. The people in the camp ran from their tents to meet them. They cried out with joy when they saw what the spies carried, sweet figs and pomegranates red as rubies and big juicy grapes. The cluster of grapes which Caleb and Joshua carried on a pole between them was so heavy the two strong men could scarcely bear its weight.

"What a wonderful land it must be!" cried the people. "Tell us about it."

But the spies would not stop to answer. They marched to where Moses sat in his tent with Aaron beside him. Then they gave their report.

"It is indeed a rich country to which you sent us," said the spies. "There is plenty of milk and honey there and grain and fruit. The fruit in the land of Canaan grows to great size like the fruit we have brought back to show you."

"Let us go to the land of Canaan tomorrow instead of starving here in the wilderness," cried the people.

"But," said several of the spies, "the people of the land are fierce fighters. They are very strong. We are tall but beside them we seemed as little as grasshoppers and they seemed big as giants. Their cities have strong walls and we could never take them in war."

"There is nothing to fear," Caleb and Joshua told Moses. "It is a good land and if the Lord is with us we can take it for our own."

But the Children of Israel would not listen to Caleb and Joshua. They were angry at Moses and turned against him as they had done so many times before.

"It would have been better to have died in Egypt," they said. "We have waited so long to enter the land of Canaan. And now we hear that the people of Canaan are too strong for us and will kill us if we try to take the land. It is surely better for us to choose a leader instead of Moses and go back to Egypt."

Suddenly a cloud filled the camp. A light shone from the cloud like a great fire. The people were afraid and hid their faces. God's voice spoke from the cloud.

"The Children of Israel do not trust My promise," said God's voice. "They were slaves so long in Egypt that they do not know how to act like brave free men. I will not let any of the older people who were slaves in Egypt enter the Promised Land except Joshua and Caleb. For they trust Me and are not afraid. But the others will wander in the wilderness for forty long years. When they are dead their children will go to live in the land of Canaan. For these children will grow up in the wilderness and they will be brave, free men and not slaves."

So one by one those who had been slaves in Egypt died in the wilderness. But the children grew strong and brave enough to live in the Promised Land.

Miriam and Aaron died and Moses was lonely. Although he was very old, he was still as strong as when he had watched the sheep in Midian. But he was very tired. He had served his people so many years. Now he was happy that God wanted to give them a new leader to bring them into the new land.

"I shall be glad to rest," said Moses.

Moses called Joshua to him and told him he would be the new leader of the Children of Israel. Joshua had served Moses for many years. He had always been faithful; he had always trusted in God. Moses knew he would make a good leader. He blessed Joshua and said: "Be strong and of good courage; you will lead the Children of Israel into the land God has promised to them. And God will be with you."

Then Moses called all his people together. He had written a beautiful song and now he repeated it to the Children of Israel. The song thanked God for His goodness and praised His greatness. Moses blessed his people and told them goodbye. They wept, for now they knew he had always been a good leader and they wanted him to lead them into the Promised Land.

But God said to Moses: "Though you will not go into the Promised Land I will let you see it from far off." So God told Moses to climb Mount Nebo which is in the land of Moab. From the mountain top Moses could see the Jordan river gleaming like silver and beyond the white city of Jericho with tall palm trees growing above its high walls. He saw also rich fields of grain and orchards of fruit trees. It was a beautiful land and Moses wept because he might not enter it.

God spoke to Moses for the last time. "This is the land," said God, "which I promised to Abraham, to Isaac and to Jacob. I will give it to their children as I have promised."

So Moses, the servant of the Lord, died in the land of Moab. No man has ever seen his grave. And from that day to this there has never been a leader in Israel like Moses, who brought his people to the gates of the Promised Land.

And Down Fell Jericho!

MOSES was dead and Joshua became the leader of the Children of Israel. God spoke to Joshua and told him what he must do.

"Moses, My servant, is dead," God said to Joshua. "All of the Children of Israel who were slaves in Egypt have also died in the wilderness. But those who remain are free people, ready to live in a free land. Now lead these people over the Jordan. Be strong and of good courage, for I will be with you wherever you go."

Then Joshua told his captains to go among the Children of Israel and say to them: "Prepare food for your journey. For in three days we will cross the Jordan to take the land God promised us."

The Children of Israel could hardly believe that their long journey in the wilderness was almost over.

Jericho was the first city in the path of the Children of Israel after they crossed the Jordan. The city had high white walls and the walls were very strong and thick. Joshua knew that if he took this city in battle, the people of Canaan would be afraid of his army and let him have their land. He was glad when God told him what to do and he did everything the Lord commanded him.

Joshua called the priests of the Children of Israel around him. He spoke first to the priests who always carried the ark before the people. This ark was a wooden box Moses had said should be made to hold the two tablets of stone on which the Ten Commandments were carved. The ark was the holiest thing that the Children of Israel had. God had said it should be carried from the wilderness into the Promised Land. Now Joshua told the priests to carry the ark like a flag for the soldiers who were to march around the city of Jericho.

Then Joshua picked out seven priests who were to blow rams' horns while they marched before the ark. He ordered them to blow upon their horns while they marched around the walls of Jericho with the soldiers. He told his armed men to march around the city with the priests but not to shout or even speak. So the priests and the soldiers made a long, long procession. Joshua gave the signal and the strange battle for Jericho began.

They marched around the city once; there was no sound but the tramp, tramp, tramp of the soldiers' feet and the blowing of the rams' horns. The people of Jericho listened behind the high, barred gates of their city. They waited for an attack. But after the priests and soldiers had marched around the city once they returned to the camp as Joshua had told them.

The second day, as Joshua commanded, the soldiers and the priests marched around the city's walls. There was no sound but the tramp, tramp, tramp of the soldiers' feet and the blowing of the rams' horns. The people of Jericho waited for an attack. They began to be afraid. The priests and soldiers marched around the city and returned to the camp.

On the third day, the soldiers and the priests marched around Jericho's high white walls, and on the fourth day, the fifth and the sixth. The priests blew their rams' horns but the soldiers of Joshua did not make a sound. For Joshua had said at the beginning: "Make no sound; do not speak. Do not even whisper. But when I tell you to shout, then you must all shout."

So for six days all who lived in the city of Jericho listened to the sound of the rams' horns and the tramp, tramp, tramp of the soldiers' feet. And they grew more and more afraid.

The seventh day came. The Children of Israel, who had made their camp before the walled city of Jericho, left their tents very early. The priests took up the ark which held the holy tablets. The seven priests took their rams' horns. The soldiers of Joshua took up their spears. Now at Joshua's command they all marched around the walls of Jericho, once, twice, seven times. The seventh time they passed around the city the priests blew louder than ever before on their rams' horns.

Then Joshua cried above the sound of the rams' horns and the tramping of the soldiers' feet: "Shout! Shout, for the Lord has given you the city of Jericho."

Every priest and soldier, every man and woman and child from the camp of Israel gave a great shout and the people of Jericho were sick with fear.

Above the sound of the rams' horns and the tramping feet and the shouts of the Children of Israel came a great noise. The strong stone walls of the city of Jericho fell flat upon the ground.

Joshua's soldiers rushed over the broken stones into the city. They shouted again and again: "The Lord has given us the city of Jericho!"

Now all the Children of Israel were glad to follow Joshua and obey him as their leader. While the people of Canaan, hearing of the fall of Jericho, grew more and more afraid.

The Strongest Man Who Ever Lived

AS his army took new land in Canaan, Joshua divided it among the tribes of Israel. He told them
they must always keep the laws God had given them in
the wilderness. Again and again he led his people
against their enemies. Joshua was the leader of the
Children of Israel until he died.

Israel still had many enemies in the land. The strongest of these were the Philistines who lived in the west of
Canaan on the shore of the Great Sea.

Samson, the strongest man who ever lived, fought all
the days of his life against the Philistines. Even in his
death he killed more of his enemies than he had in his

whole life.

There was a woman among the Children of Israel who was very sad because she had no child. But one day she came to her husband and said: "The angel of the Lord came to me and told me I would have a son. The angel said I must bring him up as a Nazirite." Then they both praised God and promised to bring up the child as they had been commanded to do.

The Nazirites were not allowed to drink strong drink. They also wore their hair long because they were forbidden to cut it. Samson's parents brought him up as a Nazirite. Each year he grew taller and stronger. When he went into the market place everyone turned to look at him. The muscles of his bare arms looked like twisted ropes; his long yellow hair fell over his broad shoulders. Because he was so strong the other young men were afraid of him. He felt that he could do anything he pleased.

When it came time for Samson to marry, he chose a woman of the Philistines for his wife. His father and his mother begged him not to take her for his wife because the Philistines were the enemies of Israel. But Samson did as he pleased, as usual.

One day Samson went down into the Philistine country to see the woman he wanted to marry. He had to pass through a wild and lonely country. A lion was hiding among the rocks. The lion sprang out suddenly and

mson to the ground. Samson felt a new
wer rushing into his large arms and
he great beast to pieces with his bare
he body back among the rocks.

way home Samson found the body of the lion
where he had left it. A swarm of bees had settled on it
and were making honey. Samson drove the bees away
and scraped the honey out of the lion's skin.

When it came time for the wedding, Samson gave a
feast for the young men among the Philistines. Everyone ate and drank and told stories and riddles. When it
came Samson's turn to tell a story or riddle, he said:

"I will tell you a riddle which will be hard to guess.
Our feast will last seven days. If any man here can guess
my riddle in the seven days of our feasting, I will pay
him thirty garments of fine linen and thirty robes of soft
wool. But if nobody can guess my riddle then you must
pay me thirty garments and thirty robes."

The young men said: "We are willing to pay you if
we cannot guess your riddle. Now tell it to us."

So Samson told them the riddle he had made. He said:

Out of the eater came forth food,
And out of the strong came forth sweetness.

The young men at the feast tried and tried to guess the
riddle but no one could guess it. Then they went to Samson's wife and said: "Coax your husband to tell you the

answer to his riddle. If we cannot find the right answer before the feasting is over, we will have to pay him thirty garments of fine linen and thirty robes of soft wool."

"But Samson would be angry if I cheated him," answered Samson's wife.

"If you will not help us," one of the Philistines told her, "we will surely burn your father's house and we will kill you and your family."

The young woman was frightened. She promised the Philistines to beg Samson to tell her the answer to his riddle.

Every day for the whole seven days the feast lasted, Samson's wife begged him to tell her the answer to the riddle no man could guess. At first he would not. But she said: "You do not love me, or you would tell me what I ask." Every day she begged him for the answer to his riddle and every day she cried and said he did not love her. So on the seventh day Samson told her and she ran to tell the young Philistines.

That night at the feast one of the Philistines told Samson: "This is the answer to your riddle:

> What is sweeter than honey?
> And what is stronger than a lion?

For from the lion who was the eater you took food, and

from the strong beast you took the sweetness of honey."

Then Samson was very angry. He killed some of the Philistines and from that time he was their enemy. He burned their grain as it stood in the fields and their olive trees. So the Philistines tried to seize him and make him their slave.

Samson knew a woman named Delilah and often came to visit her. When the Philistines heard this, some of their leaders came to Delilah and said: "We want to know what makes Samson so strong. If we knew what made him strong, we could seize him. If you find this out for us, we will each give you eleven hundred pieces of silver."

So Delilah tried to find out what made Samson so strong. He told her that if he were bound with seven new strings, he would become as weak as any other man. Delilah hid some Philistines in the inner room of her house. She said to Samson: "I will find out if you told me the truth." She bound him with seven fresh strings; then she told him that the Philistines had come into her house and were ready to seize him. Samson laughed and broke the strings which bound him.

Delilah was angry and said: "You did not tell me the truth." So Samson told her to bind him with seven new ropes and he would be as weak as any other man. But when she told him the Philistines were coming, he broke the ropes as easily as if they were thin threads.

Then Samson said: "If you weave the seven locks of my hair, I am like any other man."

Delilah was very, very angry when Samson fooled her for the third time. Day after day she coaxed him to tell her the truth. At last Samson grew tired of her coaxing.

"There has never been a razor upon my head," Samson told Delilah. "For I have been brought up as a Nazirite. The Nazirites never cut their hair. But if my head is shaved, I will not be strong any more. I will be like any other man."

So Delilah told the Philistine leaders to hide in her house again. She played her harp and sang to Samson until he fell asleep. Then she cut off all the long yellow hair which fell to his shoulders. "The Philistines are coming, Samson!" Delilah cried.

Samson woke and sprang to his feet. When the Philistines rushed from the inner room, he tried to fight them. But he had told Delilah the truth. When his head was shaven he was as weak as any other man. The Philistines bound Samson with chains and took him to prison.

But even when Samson was a weak man in prison, the Philistines were afraid of him. They put out both his eyes and kept him bound with brass chains.

The Philistines came from all parts of their country to look at Samson. They said: "He killed many of our people and was our enemy. But now he is weak and in prison. Our god has made him our prisoner."

They had a great feast in honor of Dagon, the god of the Philistines. The tables were spread in a large marble hall; the roof was held up by many pillars of marble painted with bright colors and hung with flowers. The Philistines ate and drank and made merry. They said: "Let Samson be brought out of the prison house. Let him stand before us that we can make fun of him for his weakness."

Samson had been in the Philistine prison a very long time. He had grown pale and thin. His hair had grown again and now fell about his shoulders.

A little boy led Samson out of the prison to the great hall for Samson could not see. Samson said to the little boy who held his hand: "Let me feel the pillars on which the roof rests. I want to lean upon them because I feel so weak and tired." The boy took Samson's hands and placed them upon two of the marble pillars. Samson stood between the two pillars. He listened to the Philistines who laughed at him.

When Samson was free and strong, he did not ask God to help him. Now he was only a blind slave and his enemies laughed at him. Samson began to pray.

"O Lord God," cried Samson, "remember me, and make me strong again only this once!"

Samson felt his hair, which had grown long, falling about his shoulders. He looked like a Nazirite again. He said to himself: "I am not a weak slave any more.

God has made me strong again that I may punish the enemies of my people."

Samson's hands shook the marble pillars as though they were thin sticks of wood. The people who were laughing at him began to scream. Samson said: "Let me die with the Philistines." He pulled the two pillars toward each other with all his might. They broke and fell. The other pillars began to tremble and suddenly the roof came crashing down upon all the Philistines who feasted in the hall. So Samson died and it was said that the enemies of Israel he had killed in his death were more than all those he had killed in his life.

The Girl with the Faithful Heart

WHILE the Children of Israel still lived in the wilderness, Moses appointed judges for each tribe. These judges were chosen because they were wise men and tried to be fair when their people quarreled and wanted somebody to settle their troubles. So after the Children of Israel came to the land of Canaan each tribe was ruled by a judge.

In the days when the judges ruled, there was a great famine in the land. There was a poor harvest. Many people in the town of Bethlehem were hungry. A certain man of Bethlehem took his wife, Naomi, and his two sons over the Jordan to the land of Moab. For there was plenty to eat for everyone in Moab.

At first Naomi was happy in her new home. Her two sons married two young women of Moab and the three families lived together in one house as people did in those days. Then Naomi's husband died. Her two sons were a great comfort to her but soon they also died. Naomi began to feel homesick for her old home in Bethlehem.

When Naomi heard that the famine was over in her own country, she said to herself: "I will go back to my own country." She called the wives of her two sons to her and kissed them goodbye. Their names were Orpah and Ruth, and Naomi loved them both dearly. They both loved Naomi, who had always been good to them. Now they cried when she told them she was going away.

Naomi took a few clothes in a bundle and food and a flask of water for the long journey. She started down the long, lonely road. Orpah stood at the door of her house and cried. But Ruth ran after Naomi and caught her hand.

"I want to go with you," said Ruth.

Naomi shook her head. "You would not be happy in Bethlehem," Naomi told Ruth. "My people, the people of Israel, are not like your people who live in Moab. Our ways are different and we have a different religion."

"Do not ask me to leave you," said Ruth. "For where

you go, I will go. Where you live, I will live. Your people shall be my people and your God shall be my God."

So Naomi and Ruth left the land of Moab and journeyed to Bethlehem.

They came to Bethlehem in the beginning of the barley harvest. Naomi had no land and was very poor. She and Ruth lived in a little house on the hill. They would have gone hungry if Moses had not given the Children of Israel a very kind law. This law said that when the farmers went over their fields to reap the harvest, the widowed and the fatherless might follow the reapers and gather up all the grain the reapers had left. Naomi and Ruth were both widows, but Naomi was too old and weak to go out into the harvest fields. So Ruth said: "Let me go out into the fields and follow the reapers. I will bring you home some grain and we will not go hungry."

Ruth rose early in the morning and went out into the fields. The owner of the field was Boaz, one of the richest men in Bethlehem. He came to the field and spoke pleasantly to his servants who were reaping the grain. Then he noticed a strange face among the women who followed the reapers and gathered the grain they left behind.

"Who is that girl in the blue robe?" Boaz asked his head servant.

"She is the girl who came back from Moab with Naomi," answered the servant. "This morning she came to me and said she wanted to follow the reapers and gather after them."

Boaz was a relative of Naomi's husband and had already heard how Ruth had given up her land and people to care for Naomi in her old age. Now he saw that Ruth was very beautiful. He watched her for a while and was glad to see that she never pushed the other women or tried to take more than her share. He noticed, too, that she did not speak or laugh loudly like the women about her.

At noon the reapers and those who followed after them stopped to rest and eat their mid-day meal. Boaz called Ruth to his side as he sat among his servants. He told her to sit down and rest; he shared his bread with her and gave her cool water to drink from his own pitcher.

Boaz said: "Do not go to another field. You are welcome here. And when you are thirsty, drink from the pitchers my servants have filled."

"You are very kind to a stranger," answered Ruth.

"I have heard how kind and faithful you were to Naomi," Boaz told Ruth, "and how for her sake you have left your father and mother and the land where you were born. May the God of Israel whom you have taken for your God reward you."

When the mid-day rest was over, Ruth and the other women began to follow the reapers again. Ruth could not understand why the reapers always seemed to drop grain right before her. She did not know that Boaz had said to his servants: "Pull out grain from your bundles and drop it near where Ruth of Moab is working." So by evening Ruth had an armful of grain to carry home to Naomi. And Ruth went to the fields of Boaz every day until the barley harvest was over.

Boaz loved Ruth and wished to marry her. This made Naomi very happy for Boaz was her husband's relative. Naomi's sons had left no children to carry on the family name when they died. But if Boaz and Ruth had children they would receive their share of the family's land and their name would live on in Israel.

Everyone in Bethlehem came to the wedding feast. The men sang the praises of Boaz who was known for his wealth and his kindness to the poor. In their songs the women praised Ruth for her beauty and her care of old Naomi, for whom she had given up her home and her own family. The wedding feast lasted for many days. The people of Bethlehem sang and danced and ate and drank and made merry.

When a son was born to Ruth and Boaz, no one could have been happier and prouder than Naomi. The neighbor women came to see the baby and they said to Naomi: "Blessed be the Lord, for sending this child. May his name be famous in Israel!"

Although Boaz had many servants, Naomi would not

allow anyone to take care of the child. She became his nurse and loved him even more than she had her own sons. For she knew that this boy would keep the family name alive in Israel. But Naomi did not know that this child's grandson would be David, the greatest and best-loved king of her people.

The Voice in the Darkness

THERE lived in the hill country a man named Elkanah and his wife Hannah. Every year he went to the town of Shiloh with his wife Hannah to sacrifice to the Lord of Israel. In Shiloh there was an altar to God and many people came there to sacrifice.

In Shiloh lived a very old man named Eli. He was a priest. He took care of the House of God where the altar stood. Eli was very sad. He had two sons who were priests. Eli hoped that when he died one of his sons could take his place. He wanted one of his sons to take care of the House of God and judge the people. But Eli's two sons were bad men. Eli knew that God would not want them to take care of His House and judge the people.

One day when Elkanah and Hannah, his wife, came to Shiloh, the woman was very sad. She stood at the door of the House of God and cried. Eli saw her crying. He went up to speak to her. Hannah saw the old man coming toward her. He had white hair and a white beard which came down to below his belt; he wore a long white robe. Hannah bowed low before him.

"Woman, why are you crying?" asked old Eli, the priest.

"I am crying because I am so sad," answered Hannah. "I have just asked the Lord to answer my prayer. But I have come to this place year after year to pray the same prayer. And the Lord God has never given me what I prayed for."

Eli was sorry for the woman who looked so pale and sad. He said to her: "Go in peace and the God of Israel give you what you have asked of Him."

Then Hannah and Elkanah went back to their home in the hill country. Hannah did not cry any more. When she fed the goats and milked the cows and when she worked in her house she sang happy songs. She believed Eli, the old priest, and was sure that God would surely give her what she had asked of him. God sent her a child and she named the boy Samuel. Hannah said: "This is the child I asked the Lord to give me."

When Samuel was about four years old, Hannah told Elkanah to gather offerings to lay upon the altar. Then Hannah and Elkanah went to Shiloh and they took the child Samuel with them.

Eli stood behind the altar. Hannah bowed low before the old priest. She took little Samuel by the hand and brought him up to Eli. "I am the woman who stood here praying," Hannah told Eli. "I prayed for this child and the Lord heard my prayer. Now I will give this child to the Lord to be His servant forever."

The old priest kissed the little boy and blessed him. He promised Hannah that he would take good care of the child and he blessed her also. Then Hannah and her husband returned to their home.

For a while little Samuel missed his mother. But Eli was very good to him. The old man often took the boy on his knee and told him stories. The people of Shiloh grew to love Samuel too. They brought him ripe fruits and sweet cakes to eat. Soon Samuel liked to stay with Eli.

Every year Hannah and Elkanah came to Shiloh to bring their sacrifice for the altar. Hannah made Samuel a little white robe like the one Eli wore. She brought the robe to Shiloh and put it on her son.

"Now you look like a little priest," she said.

"He will be a priest and take care of the altar and judge the people," Eli told Hannah. "I know my sons

will never be good enough to serve the Lord after I die.
But this child will take my place before the Lord." He
blessed Hannah and said: "Because you have given
your only son to serve the Lord, He will make you
happy."

God blessed Hannah and sent her more children. She
had three sons and two daughters. So she was not lonely
for the little boy in Shiloh. But she never forgot him and
every year when she went to Shiloh, she brought Samuel
a white robe. Each year she had to make the robe bigger
because Samuel grew so fast.

Eli was now very old and weak. His sons grew more
and more wicked. Eli hoped that Samuel would be good
enough to serve the Lord. But how could he tell?

One night Eli went to his bed in an inner room in the
House of the Lord. Young Samuel lay down before the
altar. The lamp burned with a low dim flame. It was
very quiet in the House of the Lord. All Samuel could
hear was the singing of the crickets in the grass outside
the open door. He was half asleep when he heard someone calling him. "Samuel!" said the voice.

Samuel thought it must be old Eli who sometimes
wanted a drink of water in the night. The priest's eyes
had grown dim; he did not like to get up and hunt for
the pitcher of water. So Samuel ran into the inner room
where Eli slept.

"Here I am," said Samuel. "Why did you call me?"

Eli woke up. "I did not call you," he answered Samuel. "You must have been dreaming. Go back to sleep."

Samuel was puzzled. He was sure Eli had called him. He went back to his place near the altar and lay down upon the ground.

"Samuel!" said the voice again.

The boy was a little frightened. He ran back to Eli and shook him by the shoulder until the old man woke up.

"Here I am," said Samuel. "I heard you calling me again."

"I did not call you, my son," Eli told him. "Lie down and try to sleep."

Samuel went back to his place near the altar. He lay down and tried to go to sleep as Eli had told him.

"Samuel!" said the voice for the third time.

The boy ran back to Eli again. This time the old man was not asleep. He had been listening in the darkness. But the voice had not called to him and he had heard nothing.

"Here I am," said Samuel. "I heard you calling me."

Then Eli was sure that the Lord was calling the child.

"Go, lie down," said Eli. "If you hear the voice again, do not come to me, because it will not be my voice."

"But what shall I say to the voice?" asked Samuel and he began to feel afraid again.

"You shall say, Speak, Lord, for Your servant hears You," answered Eli.

Samuel went back to his place near the altar. This time he did not try to sleep. He waited and soon he heard the voice again.

"Samuel, Samuel," said the voice through the darkness, for the lamp had gone out and there was no light in the House.

At first Samuel could not answer. But he knew he must speak the words that Eli had told him to say.

"Speak, Lord, for Your servant hears You," said Samuel.

"I will judge the family of Eli," said the voice, "and I will punish his two sons. For they are wicked men and they are not fit to serve Me."

The voice spoke no more. Samuel could hear the crickets singing in the grass, but there was no other sound.

The next morning Eli said to Samuel: "What did the Lord say to you last night?"

Samuel told him all the Lord had said.

Eli was sad because he loved his two sons although they were wicked men. Now he was sure that they would never serve God before His altar.

"The Lord has called you," Eli said to Samuel. "I know now that when I die you will serve God before His altar and be a good judge over the people."

Soon Eli's two wicked sons died and Eli, who was very old, died also. Then Samuel served God before His altar and was priest instead of Eli. He became a judge over the people and judged the Children of Israel all the days of his life.

A King over Israel

FOR many years Samuel judged the Children of Israel. But when he was very old, the people came to him and said:

"You are old and soon you will die. We do not want to have another judge to tell us what to do. We want a king to rule over us."

"You should have no king but God," answered Samuel.

"We want a king like the nations around us!" cried the people.

Then God spoke to Samuel. "If the Children of Israel are so foolish that they want a king," said God, "I will

127

show you which man to choose." Then God led Samuel to Saul, of the tribe of Benjamin. Saul was a strong young man; he stood head and shoulders above all the people. He looked like a mighty fighter and the Children of Israel were glad when Samuel made him their king. They wanted a brave captain to lead them against the Philistines.

Saul was a strong fighter. He led the Children of Israel against their enemies and won many battles. But as long as Saul was king the Philistines made war on Israel.

God spoke to King Saul through Samuel. But now that Saul was king over Israel he did not think he had to obey what the old priest told him.

Samuel was not afraid of Saul even though Saul was now king. "Because you put away the commands of the Lord," Samuel told Saul, "the Lord will put you away and you will not be a king any longer."

Saul was afraid. "Forgive me," he cried, "and ask the Lord to forgive me."

Samuel turned to leave Saul. Saul caught the old man's robe to make him stay and listen. The priest pulled away; a piece of the robe tore off and fell upon the ground.

"The Lord will tear away the kingdom of Israel from you," said Samuel, "as you have torn off a piece of my robe."

Saul was so frightened and sad that he grew sick. His servants said to him as he lay upon his bed: "Let us bring someone to play the harp for you. If you hear sweet music, you will be well and happy again."

The servants brought a harp player into Saul's room. He was just a shepherd boy with golden hair and rosy cheeks. He came from Bethlehem. God had told Samuel that David would be king over Israel some day. But Saul did not know that David would be king. He told him to play upon his harp.

Then David played upon his harp and he sang a song he had made while he watched his father's sheep in the pastures near Bethlehem. David sang:

> The Lord is my Shepherd; I shall not want.
> He maketh me to lie down in green pastures;
> He leadeth me beside the still waters.

When Saul heard David's song he was not afraid any more. He was sure God would take care of him the way a kind shepherd takes care of his sheep. Saul's eyes closed; he lay back on his pillows and fell asleep. David tiptoed from the room. He went back to Bethlehem to take care of his father's sheep.

The Shepherd Boy from Bethlehem

ONE day the Philistines called their soldiers together on the mountain side. King Saul called
the soldiers of Israel together on the mountain on the
other side of the valley. Suddenly a soldier came out of
the Philistine camp. He was a giant over nine feet tall.
He wore a cap of brass and a heavy coat made out of
round pieces of brass; his sword was so heavy that no
other man could carry it.

The giant was named Goliath. He walked boldly up
and down before Saul and his soldiers. "Choose a man
from your army and let him come down and fight me!"
Goliath cried to Saul in a voice like thunder. "If he

fights with me and kills me, the Philistines will be your slaves. If I kill the man from your army, then you will all be slaves of the Philistines."

When Saul and the soldiers of Israel heard Goliath's words, they were all afraid.

At this time David was home in Bethlehem, taking care of his father's sheep. David was his youngest son.

David's father called the boy to him and said:

"David, you know that your three oldest brothers are in Saul's army. I am sure your brothers do not get enough to eat in the army. They will be glad to get some food from home. Take these ten loaves of bread to your brothers. Tell them I hope they will come home soon. Take these cheeses to their captain for a present."

David put the food in a basket and left his father's house in Bethlehem. When he reached the camp of the Children of Israel, he asked everyone where to find his brothers. At last David found his three brothers. He gave them the food and stood and talked to them. While they were talking, Goliath came down from the Philistine camp. The giant stood in the valley between the two armies. He laughed at the men of Israel because they were afraid to come out and fight him.

"Who is that man?" David asked his brothers.

"He is the Philistine giant, Goliath," answered David's brothers. "For forty days he has walked before our camp, laughing at us, and daring someone to come out and fight him."

"King Saul has promised great riches to the man who kills Goliath," said the captain. "And the man who kills this giant, who has shamed Israel for forty days, is promised King Saul's daughter for his wife."

"I should like to meet Goliath in battle," said David.

This made the oldest brother angry. "Go back and take care of your sheep," he said to David. "You are a shepherd, not a soldier."

David's three brothers began to tease him. They thought that if they and the other soldiers were afraid of the terrible giant, it was silly of their little brother to want to fight him.

But the captain told King Saul what David had said. The king sent for David.

"How can you fight this Philistine?" said Saul. "You are a young boy and have never been in battle. But he has been a soldier for many years and is stronger than ten strong men."

"Once when I watched my father's sheep," answered David, "a lion tried to carry off a young lamb. I killed the lion. And another time a bear came down on the sheep and I killed him also. The Lord saved me from the lion and the bear. The Lord will save me from this strong Philistine."

"Go and fight Goliath," said Saul, "and the Lord will be with you."

King Saul gave David his own cap of brass and his coat made of round pieces of brass and his own sword.

"I cannot wear these things," said David, "they are too heavy for me."

Then David ran to the little brook that flowed down the mountain side. He picked up five round stones from the bottom of the brook and put them in the bag which hung from his belt. In one hand he carried his sling; in the other his shepherd's staff.

The giant in his brass coat came closer to the camp. His sword flashed in the bright sunshine. David was not afraid. He ran out and stood before the giant.

At first Goliath thought he must be dreaming. Not even King Saul who was the tallest and strongest of all the soldiers of Israel dared to come out and fight him. And here was a young, weak boy who did not even have a sword, but carried a shepherd's staff in his hand.

Goliath laughed long and loud. Then he became angry. "Do you think that I am a dog? Why do you come out with a stick to beat me?" he roared.

But David was not afraid. He said: "You come to me with a sword. But I come to you in the name of the Lord God of the armies of Israel. You have made fun of Israel. Now all the earth will know that God does not save with the sword. He will make me strong and I will kill you!"

The giant waved his bright, big sword and rushed toward David. David took one of the stones and fitted it into his sling. He took careful aim. The stone hit Goliath right in the forehead. The giant bent and shook like a great tree in a storm. He fell upon his face and lay still at David's feet.

When the Philistines saw that their strongest soldier was dead, they became wild with fear. They started to run away. Saul and his soldiers followed them to the gates of their city. The soldiers of Israel killed many of their enemies that day. Every man grew rich from the treasures they found in the Philistine camp on the mountain side.

David was brought before Saul that the king might reward him. On that day David first met Saul's son, Jonathan. The two boys looked into each other's eyes; Jonathan held out his hand and David took it and held it tightly. From that moment they were true friends.

David still wore his plain white shepherd robe; Jonathan, the king's son, wore a cloak of purple with a belt of gold. Jonathan took off his cloak and put it around David's shoulders. Then he gave David his belt of heavy gold, his sword and his bow. Jonathan said: "David, I know my father will reward you for what you have done for Israel this day. But I want to give you these things because I love you as my own soul."

Saul made David one of his captains. He tried not to be jealous of the shepherd boy. But he could not forget how everyone praised David for killing the giant. He remembered that the women came out of all the cities, playing on their timbrils and singing:

> Saul hath slain his thousands,
> And David his ten thousands.

Saul listened and after that he often said to himself:

"The people praise David more than me. Soon they will want him to be their king."

So Saul began to hate David; he even planned to kill him. Jonathan told David he must go away. They wept when they said goodbye because they loved each other so dearly.

David went from place to place, for he knew that Saul wanted to kill him. He often thought of the pastures near Bethlehem where he had watched his father's sheep. Now he did not dare to go home.

Saul was a brave soldier and fought the Philistines until the day of his death. He died in a battle in the mountains and Jonathan died the same day. The men of Israel had always remembered what a strong fighter David was. Now they asked him to become their king.

David was sad when he heard that his dearest friend, Jonathan was dead. He wrote a beautiful poem telling of their friendship. David had been a shepherd and a poet and a soldier; now he was a king. He took a strong city on the hills and called it Jerusalem. King David lived there forty years and ruled over Israel. To this day Jerusalem is called the City of David.

The Wisest of Kings

KING David ruled over Israel for forty years. David had many sons, and, of course, all of them wanted to be made king in their father's place. But David picked out his son Solomon to be the next king. Solomon's name means peace. David hoped that Solomon would rule over Israel in peace for many years.

Jerusalem, the city of David, was now the greatest city in all Israel. David wanted to build a Temple in Jerusalem, where the people from all over the land could come to offer sacrifice. But God Who loves peace did not want His Temple built by a man who had been a soldier. He wanted His Temple to be built by a man of peace.

David said: "My son, Solomon, who is a man of peace, will build the House of God on Mount Zion."

King David died and was buried in Jerusalem. Then Solomon was king over all Israel.

King Solomon dreamed that God spoke to him and said: "What gift can I give you?"

Solomon answered God: "O God, You have made me king instead of David, my father. I am very young and I do not know what to do. How can I rule this great people? O God, if You wish to give me a gift, give me wisdom that I may be a good and wise king."

"Because you have not asked for long life," God answered Solomon in his dream, "and have not asked Me for riches, I will give you a wise heart. You will be wiser than any man who has ever lived; you will be wiser than any man who will come after you. I will also give you more riches than any king in Israel ever had before, and a long and honored life."

King Solomon awoke, and knew it was only a dream. But God kept his promise to Solomon. God not only gave Solomon great riches and a long life, but the gift of wisdom.

There were no judges in Israel any more and the king judged all the people who came to him to settle their quarrels. Solomon had been king for just a little while when two women came to him as he sat on his high throne to judge the people.

One woman was dressed in a bright blue robe. She had long dark hair and walked proudly. The other woman was dressed in a yellow robe. Her hair was golden and she would have been very beautiful if her eyes had not been red with crying. Behind the two walked an old woman, who wore the plain dark dress of a slave. This old woman carried a beautiful baby boy in her arms. The child was asleep; he did not look more than two or three days old.

The proud woman in the blue robe spoke first. Her voice was so loud and angry that the baby woke up and began to cry. The woman in the yellow dress tried to take the baby from the slave and quiet it. But Solomon told the slave to lay the child at the foot of his throne. Then he listened to the angry woman.

"O king," she began, "this woman and I live in the same house. First my baby boy was born; three days after she had a little son. This old slave took care of us and our babies. But last night she left us and did not come back to the house until this morning. In the night this woman's baby died. I was sound asleep. She came and left the dead child near my pillow. Then she took my child, who was alive and well, back to her own bed. When I woke in the morning, I saw that she had taken my child and left the one who was dead in its place."

"No, King Solomon!" cried the fair-haired woman. "This woman does not speak the truth. It is my child who is lying at your feet. For her child died in the night."

King Solomon turned to the old slave. "You have seen both of the babies and taken care of them," he said. "Now tell me who is the true mother of this child."

The slave woman shook her head. "I am very old," she answered, "and my eyes are so dim that I cannot even tell the light from the darkness. How can I say who is the true mother of this babe?"

At first King Solomon did not know what to do. The two mothers fell upon their knees before his throne and begged for the child. This was the first time he had acted as a judge. God had promised him wisdom but he did not feel wise enough to say who should have the boy. The baby began to cry again. There was no other sound in the great hall. Everybody was very quiet and listened to what the king might say.

At last King Solomon spoke. He turned to one of his soldiers who stood beside the throne. "Take up the child," commanded King Solomon.

The soldier bent down and took up the child.

King Solomon spoke to the two mothers. "I do not know which of you is telling the truth," he told them. "And this blind old slave woman cannot be a witness for either of you. Draw your sword," King Solmon said to the soldier who held the child.

The soldier drew his shining sword.

"I will try to satisfy both of you," King Solomon said to the two women. "He will cut the child in half with his sword. He will give half to one of you and half to the other."

The woman with the bright golden hair tried to take the baby from the soldier. The soldier pushed her back; but she held tightly to his arm which held the sword.

"O my lord," she cried to the king, "do not kill my baby. I do not want this wicked woman to have my son. But to save his life I am willing to give him up."

"What do you say?" Solomon asked the tall proud woman in the blue robe.

"I will never let her have the child while he lives," answered the woman. "If it is the king's will, let neither of us have the child. I would rather have him killed than let this woman have him."

"Now I will judge between you," said King Solomon. "The woman who loved this child so much that she would give him up is the true mother."

The mother took the baby from the soldier and held it tightly in her arms. She kissed the baby and thanked King Solomon for giving her back her child. All the people who heard of the judgment of Solomon praised the king for his wisdom.

Soon the wisdom of Solomon became known through all Israel. People in faraway lands heard of the wise king. Even the Queen of faraway Sheba took the long journey over land and sea that she might talk with him. She said to Solomon: "In my own land I heard of your wisdom. But no one praised you enough. Your people are happy that they have such a wise and strong king." She gave King Solomon many presents; she gave him gold and jewels and spices. Then the Queen of Sheba returned to her own land, praising the great King of Israel.

Solomon had another friend, King Hiram of Tyre. King Hiram sent Solomon gold and jewels and sweet-smelling sandal wood. Hiram also sent Solomon wood from the cedar and cypress trees. Hiram sent his best workmen to work with the Children of Israel and help them build the House of God.

The House of God was called the Temple. It stood on Zion, one of the high hills of Jerusalem. The walls were of shining white marble; the roof was of rare wood. The walls and the beams of the roof were decorated with pure gold. The doors were of gold and here and there were decorations of stones of great value. The great altar was of brass. There were also ten large branched candlesticks made of pure gold. The cups and bowls which the priests used in the service were also made of gold. It was the most beautiful building in the whole world.

When the Temple was finished the priests brought the Ark through the great golden doors. The Children of Israel had carried the Ark before them while they wandered in the desert. In this box were the two tablets of stone on which Moses had written the Ten Commandments. Now the priests placed the Ark in the House of God. At both ends of the Ark were golden figures of angels; their bright, drooping wings covered the Ark and seemed to bless it.

All the people of Jerusalem, and those who had come from miles around, gathered in the courts of the Temple. The priests, dressed in fine linen, stood before the altar. A hundred and twenty priests blew upon their long trumpets; others played upon cymbals, and others sang. There seemed to be only one voice in the great and beautiful House of God as they sang the song, which we still sing today: "Praise the Lord, for He is good, for His mercy endureth forever."

After many, many years the enemies of Israel burned the Temple at Jerusalem to the ground. But the Children of Israel never forgot how beautiful it was when Solomon was king. Even to this day no matter in what land they live, the Children of Israel always turn their faces toward Jerusalem, when they come to God in prayer.

Elijah the Good Prophet

ONCE there was a prophet sent to teach the Children of Israel; his name was Elijah. The prophets listened to the voice of God and God told them what to do. Elijah was like the other prophets; he obeyed God and was not afraid of anyone, not even the king. In the days of Elijah a king named Ahab ruled the country. Ahab was a very wicked king. He was cruel to the poor; he did not obey God but even made sacrifices to the gods of his wife's country. When Elijah told King Ahab that God would punish him, the king tried to kill him.

Then the word of the Lord came to Elijah, saying:

"Go and hide yourself in the wilderness. I will take care of you there."

Elijah went to hide himself in the wilderness. He drank water from a little brook that ran between the rocks. "But there is nothing to eat!" he cried.

Then God sent some ravens to feed Elijah. Every morning and every night the big, black birds flew down to a pile of rocks beside the brook. In their beaks they carried bread and meat for Elijah. He lived in the wilderness for many days.

The little brook dried up for there was no rain. Elijah had no water to drink. God said: "Leave the wilderness and walk until you come to the next town. There you will find a poor woman without a husband. This widow will take care of you."

When Elijah reached the gates of the town, he saw a woman gathering sticks.

"Will you give me some water to drink?" asked Elijah.

The woman went to the well beside the gate; Elijah called after her.

"And will you give me a bit of bread to eat?" he asked.

"I am sorry," said the woman, "but I have no bread to give you. My husband is dead; I am a poor widow who has hardly anything left in the house to eat. There is no rain and nothing will grow. If God does not help me soon my little son and I will surely die of hunger."

"God will take care of you," Elijah told the widow.

They walked to the poor, small house where the widow lived with her little boy. The woman showed Elijah the handful of dry sticks which she had picked up.

"I gathered these sticks to make a fire to cook our breakfast," she said.

Her little boy stood at the door. He was pale and thin. "Mother, I am hungry," he said. "Won't you give me a piece of bread to eat?"

"I have no bread," answered his mother. She showed Elijah a jar and a jug which stood on the table. "There is just a handful of meal in the jar," she said, "and a little oil in the jug. When I have used this meal and oil, we will have nothing more to eat."

"God will take care of you," said Elijah. "Make a fire in your oven with the sticks you carry and bake me bread out of the meal and oil. Then cook breakfast for yourself and your son."

"There is just enough meal and oil left for one little loaf of bread," the widow answered. "If I give it to you, what will my son and I have to eat?"

Elijah told her what God had promised him: "There will always be meal in your jar and oil in your jug, until the Lord sends rain upon the land again. After that you and your child will have plenty to eat."

The widow mixed the oil and meal and made Elijah a little flat loaf of bread which she baked in the stone oven outside her house. Elijah began to eat the bread while it was still hot for he was very hungry. The little boy was angry because he was hungry, too.

"Mother," said the widow's son, almost crying, "you gave bread to this man, and now we have nothing to eat. You took all the meal and oil we had in the house."

"Look in the jar," Elijah told the little boy.

"There is still some meal in it," said the little boy.

"Now look in the jug," said Elijah. "Is it empty?"

"I know my mother poured out all the oil," answered the child, "but now I can see some oil in the jug."

God kept his promise to Elijah and he and the widow and her son had enough to eat until the rain came again upon the land.

Then Elijah left the widow's house. He did many wonderful things; but I have time to tell you just one more story about the good prophet.

There was another prophet among the Children of Israel. His name was Elisha and he also did many wonderful things. Elijah grew old and knew that soon he would die and be with God. The prophet wondered who would take his place among the Children of Israel.

The day came when Elijah knew he must leave this earth forever. Elijah and his pupil, Elisha, walked together along the road which led to Bethel. It was a long way to Bethel. The day was hot and Elijah saw that Elisha looked tired. So he said: "The Lord wishes me to go as far as Bethel. But you do not have to go. Sit down in the shadow of those great rocks and rest."

But Elisha answered: "I will not leave you."

The two prophets traveled to Bethel. When they reached Bethel, they met some of Elijah's pupils. They said to Elisha: "It is said that the Lord will take our master, Elijah, away from us today. So stay with us."

Elisha answered: "I know the Lord will take away our master. But do not ask me to stay here with you."

Then Elijah turned and put his hand on Elisha's arm. "Elisha," he said, "it would be better for you to stay here with your friends. The Lord has told me to go as far as Jericho."

Elisha had always obeyed the older prophet. But now he could not bear to be left behind. "I will go the rest of the way with you," said Elisha.

At last they came to Jericho, the beautiful white city with tall palm trees growing in every street. As they reached the gates of the city, pupils of Elijah came out into the road and waited for the two men.

"Stay with us," they all cried to Elisha, "for surely the Lord will take the master away from you today."

And Elijah turned to Elisha and said: "Stay here at

Jericho. For the Lord has commanded me to go as far as the Jordan."

But Elisha shook his head and answered his old teacher: "I will go with you as far as the Jordan."

So the two walked on together, hand in hand, until at last they reached the banks of the Jordan. Fifty of the pupils of Elijah followed them; they stood watching from a little distance. They wondered who would be their leader if God took Elijah away.

Elijah took off his long brown cloak, which he always wore, and struck the waters. The water of the river divided. The old prophet, Elijah, and the young prophet, Elisha, walked between the waters on the dry river bed until they reached the other shore. Elijah drew Elisha to him; he kissed the young man and blessed him.

"You have always been obedient and faithful to me," said Elijah. "I wish I could give you some gift before God takes me away."

"You have given a good gift to all your pupils, my master," answered Elisha. "You have given them a part of your great wisdom. But even if they are wise and good, I wonder who will lead them and teach them after you are gone. If you think I am wise and good enough to lead them after you are gone, give me twice the wisdom you have given them."

Elijah said: "I do not know how much of my wisdom I can give you. I do not know who will take my place. But if you see me when God takes me away, that will be a sign that you are wise and good enough to lead my pupils."

They stood close together, but suddenly a great wind rushed between them. Flames of fire rose on the bank of the Jordan where Elijah and Elisha stood. The pupils who watched from afar were afraid. They fell upon the ground and covered their eyes with their cloaks. But Elisha stood upright and held out his hands to his dear master.

Then through the flames Elisha saw a chariot of fire, drawn by two horses of fire. Elijah stepped into the fiery chariot and waved his hand in farewell. Elijah pulled off his long brown cloak and dropped it at Elisha's feet. Through clouds of fire the flaming chariot slowly rose toward the sky.

"My father, my father!" cried Elisha. He wept for he knew that he would never see his dear master again or hear his voice as long as he lived.

Elisha picked up Elijah's cloak and struck the waters with it. The waves of the river divided as they had done before, and Elisha walked on dry ground back to the other side of the Jordan.

Now the men who had watched from far off came down to the river bank. Elisha put on his master's cloak and the pupils of Elijah bowed down before the young man. They said: "We saw you cross the river. Elijah has given you his cloak. We know it is a sign that you are good and wise enough to take Elijah's place in Israel."

The Man Who Tried to Run Away from God

THERE were many prophets in Israel like Elijah and Elisha who listened to God's voice and gave His message to the people. One of the prophets did not want to obey God. He did not want to teach the people in other countries to be good. This prophet was named Jonah.

The great and strong city of Nineveh was many miles from Israel. It was the wickedest city in the world. God was sorry for the people of Nineveh. He knew that if they did not become good they must be punished. So God called the prophet, Jonah, to Him. God said to Jonah: "Go to Nineveh and tell the people I am tired of their wickedness. Tell them they will be punished unless they obey Me."

Jonah said to himself: "Why should I go to Nineveh and save the people there? They are not my people. I will run away from God. Perhaps He will send someone else to Nineveh."

So Jonah went down to the city of Joppa on the shore of the Great Sea. A ship was ready to sail to a faraway country. Jonah paid his fare and got on the ship. "This ship will take me many, many miles from Nineveh," thought Jonah.

As soon as the ship set sail a great storm rose. The waves were so high that the sailors were afraid their wooden ship would be broken and they would all drown. The ship was loaded with boxes of goods to sell in far countries. The sailors threw the boxes into the sea to make the ship lighter, but it still tossed from side to side on the high waves. The storm grew more and more terrible.

The rocking of the boat made Jonah sick. He lay in the captain's cabin, too weak to lift up his head. The sailors did not get sick because they were used to rough weather on the Great Sea. But they had never seen a storm like this. They grew more and more frightened.

"What can we do to save ourselves?" cried the sailors.

The captain of the ship was frightened, too. But he

did not let the sailors know how frightened he was. "Sometimes," said the captain to the sailors, "there is a storm like this because there is a wicked person on the ship."

"Who can that person be?" cried the sailors.

"I do not know," answered the captain, "but if we draw lots, we will find out. Let every man write his name upon a piece of paper. We will throw all the papers into this bowl. I will draw out one piece. The man whose name is written on it will be the one who has brought this trouble on us."

The sailors all wrote their names upon pieces of paper and threw them into the large clay bowl that stood at the captain's feet. The captain looked about him.

"Has every man on the ship dropped his lot into the bowl?" he asked.

"No," answered an old sailor. "There is the man who came on the ship at Joppa. He is sick and is resting in your cabin."

"Bring him on deck at once," said the captain.

The sailor brought Jonah up to the deck where they all stood and waited. The captain told Jonah to write his name on his lot and throw it with the others in the bowl. Every man held his breath while the captain drew a piece of paper from the clay bowl. He read the name on it and then spoke slowly. "This is the lot which

Jonah threw into the bowl," he said. "Are you the wicked man who has brought this storm upon us?"

Then Jonah knew that he could not run away from God. He said: "Yes, I have disobeyed my God and tried to run away from Him. This storm has come because of my disobedience. Why should the ship be wrecked and you all drown for my sin? Throw me into the sea and the storm will die down and the sea will be calm again."

But the sailors did not want to throw Jonah into the angry sea. They thought he would surely drown. They tried again to take up their oars and row to the shore. But the sea grew more and more stormy. Then they knew there was no other way to save themselves from drowning. They said: "May your God forgive us for doing this thing. But the captain drew the lot with Jonah's name. And Jonah has said that he has sinned and the storm has come upon us because of his disobedience." So they threw Jonah into the sea.

Jonah could not swim. He thought he would surely drown. But God sent a great fish to swallow Jonah. Then Jonah knew that God had forgiven him and would save him. For three days and three nights the great fish swam through the waves of the Great Sea. Then it swam to the shore and opened its wide mouth and Jonah jumped out upon the dry land.

Now when God again told Jonah to go to Nineveh,

the prophet did not dare to disobey Him. Jonah took the long journey to the wicked city and stood in the middle of the market place. He cried in a loud voice: "In forty days God will destroy the wicked people of Nineveh." Everybody stopped to listen. Jonah told them that if they would show they were sorry and would try to be good, God would forgive them.

The people of Nineveh listened to Jonah and believed his words. Even the king upon his golden throne asked God to forgive him.

Jonah was not glad that the people of Nineveh had turned to God and promised to be good. He said to himself: "Nineveh is a very wicked city; it should be punished. Why should God forgive these people?"

God knew that Jonah should not be so unforgiving and cruel. So, when Jonah sat at the gates of the city, God caused a vine to spring up beside him. The vine grew quickly; soon it grew above Jonah's head. There were broad, wide leaves growing on the vine. The leaves spread over Jonah like an umbrella and kept off the heat of the noonday sun. Jonah was glad to sit in the pleasant shade.

But the next morning God sent a worm to eat the roots of the vine. The leaves began to turn brown; they dried up and fell to the ground. Then the stalk dried up. A hot wind blew from the desert. The noonday sun sent its hot rays on Jonah's head as he sat by the gate. If he only had the broad, green leaves of the vine over his head again!

Jonah was very angry. "O Lord!" he cried, "why did you kill that beautiful vine which grew near the gate?"

God heard Jonah and answered him. "Are you angry because you do not have the vine to give you shade any more?" God said to Jonah.

"I miss the shade," Jonah said. "And I am sorry for the vine. It was so beautiful and you killed it."

"Jonah," God told him, "you are a very foolish man. I did this to make you understand why I tried so hard to save the city of Nineveh. You are sorry for the vine which grew up in just one night. But you did not plant it or water it to make it grow. The people of Nineveh are my children. I gave them life and took care of them. That is why I was so sorry for them and wanted to save them."

How God Saved a Good Man from the Lions

THE prophets often told the people that if they did not keep God's laws, He would take their country from them. After King Solmon died, his kingdom was divided. The tribes which lived in the north of Palestine called themselves Israel. The Kingdom of Judah was in the south. Its greatest city was Jerusalem.

A strong enemy came and made war against the Kingdom of Israel. The enemy took away Israel and the other tribes and nobody ever heard of them again.

For many years the Kingdom of Judah was strong enough to fight its enemies. But one day the Babylonian armies camped on the hills around Jerusalem. The Babylonians were too strong for the people of Judah. They entered the city of Jerusalem and burned the beautiful Temple; the king of Babylon carried off the golden vessels from the Temple and placed them in the house of his gods in his own country. The men, women and children of the Kingdom of Judah were taken to Babylon where they lived for many years. They were called Jews because they had come from the tribe of Judah.

Among the Jews in Babylon there was a man named Daniel. Because he was wise enough to tell the king of Babylon the meaning of his dreams, the king rewarded Daniel. He gave Daniel a robe of purple, such as kings wear, and a golden chain.

Then Darius became king. He also was Daniel's friend; he made Daniel the ruler over his governors. The governors were jealous of Daniel. They could not rest until they found a way to make the king angry with him.

The wicked governors knew that Daniel was a faithful Jew and prayed to the God of his people even in Babylon.

The governors went before King Darius. They bowed low and one of them said: "May the king live forever! Your governors have talked together and they think you should make a new law."

"What law do you think I should make?" asked King Darius.

"King Darius is the greatest of kings," said the governor, bowing again. "You, O King, can grant the wish of any man in your kingdom. It is not right that anybody in Babylon should ask another king or god for anything. Your governors think it would be a fine thing if you made a law forbidding any man to pray to his gods for thirty days. And we think you should also say that if any man in Babylon disobeys you in this, he will be thrown into a den of hungry lions."

Then Darius ordered the law to be set down in writing and signed it with his name.

Daniel heard of the new law. He did not like to disobey the king but he knew he must pray to God as he had done all his life. Three times a day Daniel went into the house that the king had given him for his own. He went to his room upstairs which had a window facing toward Jerusalem. Here three times a day Daniel prayed to God to take care of him and gave thanks for all His goodness.

The wicked governors knew that Daniel prayed to his God three times a day. They hid in his house while he was praying; they seized him and took him before the king. They said: "O King, this man has disobeyed your new law and has prayed to his own God. Is it not right that he should be thrown into a den of lions?"

King Darius loved Daniel and did not want to see him thrown into a den of lions. He told the governors that it would be wrong to kill a good man like Daniel. But they said: "O King, we do not need to tell you that in this land the king cannot change a law that he has made."

Darius knew they spoke the truth. Not even he could change a law that he had signed. He was very sad when he told his soldiers to throw Daniel into the lions' den.

The lions were kept in a den at the foot of the king's palace garden. There was a heavy iron gate across the mouth of the den. The soldiers opened the gate and pushed Daniel through.

One of Daniel's enemies said: "Perhaps one of Daniel's friends may drop a sword or a knife through the bars of this gate, so he can fight the lions."

So the king ordered his soldiers to put a heavy stone across the gate at the mouth of the den. Then Darius sealed the gate with his own seal. Now the wicked governors were happy; they knew nobody would dare to break the king's seal and lift the stone. They were sure nobody could help Daniel who would surely be torn to pieces by the hungry lions.

Darius also thought that his friend Daniel would surely die. He went back to his palace. He could not eat or sleep. All night he lay awake upon his couch of ivory and gold. He was glad when the night was over and the first rays of the sun began to steal through the windows of his room.

The king rose from his couch and hurried out into the garden. Even before he came to the den, Darius called out to see whether Daniel was still alive. He cried: "O Daniel, could the God you serve save you from the lions?"

There was no answer. Darius climbed upon the great stone at the mouth of the den, but he could hear nothing. He called to his servants who stood waiting in the palace garden. "Come quickly and lift the stone!"

The servants lifted the heavy stone. Darius leaned over the bars of the iron gate and called again: "O Daniel, could the God you serve save you from the lions?"

Then Daniel's voice came up from the darkness of the lions' den: "My God sent an angel to shut the lions' mouths. They have not hurt me."

King Darius was very happy. He commanded his servants to lift Daniel out of the lions' den. When Daniel stood before Darius, the king saw that he was not hurt at all because he trusted God. The lions had not even torn his purple robe. Then Darius praised the God of Daniel. He said: "He is the living God, Who has delivered Daniel from the power of the lions."

A Jewish Girl Saves Her People

AFTER the Jews were driven from Jerusalem, they went to many lands. Some Jews went to live in Persia. The Persians treated them kindly.

Mordecai was a Jew who lived in Persia. His young cousin lived in his house. Her parents were dead and Mordecai treated her like his own daughter. She was as sweet and beautiful as the myrtle; Mordecai gave her the Hebrew name of the flower, which is Hadassah. But the Persians named her Esther, which means a star. Today we always call her Esther because she shone like a star in the darkness, when her people needed her help.

Ahasuerus was king of Persia. He sent messengers

to the east and to the west. He sent messengers to the north and to the south of his kingdom. The messengers went to every house in every big city and small town in Persia. Whenever the king's messengers found a young girl, they took her to the king's palace in the city of Shushan. For Ahasuerus, king over Persia, wanted a wife. He told his messengers to bring all the girls of Persia together that he might choose one of them to be his queen.

Mordecai and his cousin lived in Shushan. When the king's messenger came to their house and told Esther she must go to the king's palace she began to cry. She told Mordecai she did not want to leave him. She wanted to stay and take care of his house. She said she knew she would miss her lovely rose garden and her pet doves.

While the messenger waited at the gate, Mordecai comforted Esther. He told her not to cry. He said she must try to live like a good Jewish girl in the king's palace.

"Before you leave me," Mordecai said to Esther, "I want you to promise to obey me, even if the king chooses you for his queen."

"I do not wish to be a queen," answered Esther, weeping. "And I will always obey you, for you have been like a father to me."

"Then listen to my words and do not forget them,"

Mordecai told Esther. "As long as you are living in the king's palace, do not tell anyone that you are my cousin. And you must not tell anyone you are a Jewess until I tell you the time has come for you to do so."

Then Esther went to live in the king's house along with all the other young girls in Persia.

At last Mordecai heard news that made him both sad and happy. King Ahasuerus had chosen Esther from among all the girls of Persia and had crowned her queen! Mordecai was sad because he was lonely for Esther; now he knew she would never live in his house again. But he was happy that a Jewess was the great king's wife. "If our people are ever in trouble, Esther will help us," Mordecai said to himself. He did not dream how soon that day would come.

Mordecai sat near the gate of the king's garden every day; he listened to the king's servants and the people of the king's court. He wanted to hear about Esther. Everyone spoke of the new queen and praised her beauty and her goodness. Then Mordecai was glad Esther was the king's wife. But he was very lonely and wished that he might see her.

One day as Mordecai sat near the gate of the king's garden, he saw two of the king's servants talking together. The servants did not see Mordecai who sat hidden behind one of the great stone pillars of the gate. Mordecai heard them planning how they would kill the king. As soon as he could, Mordecai sent word to his cousin Esther. Esther told the king that the two wicked servants planned to kill him. She also told him that a Jew named Mordecai had warned her of the servants' plans. The two servants were hanged for trying to kill their king. Then King Ahasuerus ordered that this should all be written down in a book. This book told what happened in the king's court.

Among the proud princes of Persia was a man named Haman, and he was the proudest of them all. King Ahasuerus made Haman the most honored man in the kingdom. The King commanded that when anyone met Prince Haman he had to bow down to the ground. This pleased Haman because he was so very proud.

One day Haman and his servants walked through the gate of the king's garden. Mordecai was sitting there; he hoped he might get news of Queen Esther. Mordecai saw that everyone who met Haman bowed down before him. But Mordecai did not get up from the place where he was seated; and he did not bow down to Haman.

Haman was very angry. He said to one of his servants: "Who is that man who does not bow down to me?"

The servant spoke to the keeper of the king's gate. The keeper of the gate had often seen Mordecai sitting there and had talked with him. The keeper of the gate answered Haman's servant: "He is called Mordecai the Jew."

Haman's servant came back to him. "My lord," he said, "the man who will not bow down to you is a Jew and his name is Mordecai."

"I will not punish Mordecai alone for not bowing down to me," said Haman to himself. "He is a Jew! Then every Jew in the whole kingdom of Persia must die because Mordecai will not do me honor."

The next time Haman stood before the king's throne, Haman said: "O king, there are people in your kingdom who have their own laws. They do not keep the king's law. They will hurt all of us if we do not kill them."

King Ahasuerus was very lazy. He trusted Haman and was glad to have him rule the country. The king did not even ask the name of the people Haman wanted to kill. He said: "Do as you think best." Then he took his ring from his finger and gave it to Haman. If anybody had this ring everyone in the whole kingdom had to obey him.

So Haman put on the king's ring and gave orders just as though he were really the king. Haman sent letters all through the kingdom telling the Persians to kill the Jews on a certain day. All of the Jews who lived in Shushan were to die also on that day. Haman gave the king's soldiers orders to kill the Jews of Shushan. He told the soldiers: "But bring Mordecai before me and my servants will hang him on a high gallows I have built in my courtyard."

The Jews of Persia heard of the letters which Haman had sent out in the king's name. They were afraid and did not know what to do. They wept and prayed and asked God to save them.

When Mordecai heard that Haman planned to kill all the Jews, he went at once to the king's gate. This time he passed through the gate into the garden and went into the king's palace. He walked through the marble halls which were hung with curtains of purple and gold. At last he found the part of the palace where his cousin Esther lived.

Esther was very glad to see Mordecai again. She began to tell him how much she missed him. She asked him why he had not come to see her before. But Mordecai did not listen to her. He told her that Haman planned to kill all the Jews of Persia on a certain day. Mordecai said that only Esther could save them.

"What can I do?" cried Esther.

"You must go to the king and ask him to make a new law that will save our people," answered Mordecai.

"I cannot go to the king until he sends for me," Esther told Mordecai. "It is the king's law that no one can come before him until he is sent for. Anyone who disobeys that law may be put to death."

"You must go to the king even if you lose your life," said Mordecai.

"If I die, I shall die for my people," Esther answered him. "Now go and tell all the Jews of Shushan to pray for me. I will go to the king even if he has not sent for me. And if I must die, I shall die."

Then Esther told her handmaidens to bring out her richest robes. The handmaidens dressed the queen and combed her long beautiful hair. They put upon her head the crown with which the king had crowned her; they put necklaces around her neck and bracelets upon her arms. Esther's handmaidens wanted to go with her, because they all loved her dearly. But she said: "If the king is angry with me and sends me to my death, why should you die also?" So Esther went all alone to King Ahasuerus although he had not sent for her.

The king sat upon his high throne in his throne room of marble and gold. At his right side and at his left stood a tall soldier with a drawn sword. In his hand the king held his golden scepter. It was known through all the court that if anybody came before the king without being sent for, and the king did not hold out his scepter, it meant death. But if the king held out his scepter that was a sign of mercy.

Esther came slowly into the throne room. She saw the soldiers with the drawn swords and she was afraid. She knew that if the king did not hold out his scepter to her, the soldiers would lead her to her death. For a moment she stood near the doorway too frightened to move. Then she walked to the throne and bowed low before the king.

At first King Ahasuerus was angry that Esther had disobeyed his law and had come to him before he sent for her. But when he saw how pale and frightened she looked and that she was weeping, he held out his scepter to her in sign of mercy. Esther knew she would not be sent to her death. She was glad that God had spared her to ask the king to save her people.

"What do you wish, Queen Esther?" asked Ahasuerus. "I will give you anything you wish, even if you ask for half my kingdom."

Esther did not know why, but she felt she should wait before she asked her husband to spare the Jews. She said: "O king, I will tell you what I wish, when you come to a banquet I will prepare for you tomorrow night. And, if it pleases the king, bring Haman also that he may eat and drink with us."

That night the king could not sleep. His servants called dancers to dance before him and harp players and singers. But King Ahasuerus sent them away. He thought he might grow sleepy if he listened to one of his slaves reading from the history book. Everything the king had done was written in this book. The slave began to read how two of the king's wicked servants had planned to kill him.

"Does it tell who brought me news of the plot and saved my life?" asked King Ahasuerus.

"Yes," answered the slave. "It was Mordecai the Jew."

"What reward did I give Mordecai the Jew?" asked the king.

The slave read over the page. "It does not say here that you gave any reward to Mordecai," he told the king.

Early the next morning the king sent for Haman and invited him to Queen Esther's banquet that evening. Haman was proud and happy to receive such an honor.

"I want you to advise me what to do," went on King Ahasuerus, "for your advice is always good. What honor can I pay to a man I wish to honor above all the other men in the kingdom?"

"Surely, the king means me," thought Haman. "First Queen Esther honors me by inviting me to a banquet with the king. Now Ahasuerus wishes to honor me above all the other men in the kingdom. What honor can I ask that will make the people of Persia think I am almost as great as the king?"

Then Haman bowed low before Ahasuerus and said:

"This is what should be done for the man the king wishes to honor: Let him be dressed in the king's own robes of purple and gold; let him ride the king's own horse. Let this man ride horseback through the whole city. And let the king order the proudest man in his whole court to lead the horse through the city and cry out in all the streets, This is the man whom the king is pleased to honor!"

Ahasuerus knew that Haman was thinking of himself. He knew how proud Haman was and wanted to tease him. "That is very good advice, Haman," answered the king. "Find Mordecai the Jew and dress him in my robes of purple and gold. Give him my horse to ride with the saddle set with silver. And you yourself will lead the horse through the city and cry out in every street, This is the man whom the king is pleased to honor!"

Haman was very angry but he did not dare to disobey the king. So he did all that the king had told him to do. But he said to himself: "Today Mordecai is honored like a king. But tomorrow he will be hanged upon the gallows I have set up for him in my courtyard."

That very night the king and Haman went to eat and drink with Queen Esther. The queen's handmaidens served them and played sweet music upon their harps. The dancing girls danced and a juggler tossed bright balls in the air and caught them to amuse the guests.

Then Esther had the slaves clear away the golden dishes and wine cups from the long table. She sent away her handmaidens and came and knelt down before the king.

"O great king," said Esther, "now I will tell you what I did not dare to tell you when I stood before your throne."

"What is your wish, my queen?" answered Ahasuerus. "I will give you what you ask, even if it is half my kingdom."

"I ask only for my life," Esther told the king.

"What do you mean?" cried the king. "Who would dare to hurt you?"

Esther pointed to Haman. "That wicked man wishes to kill all the Jews of Persia," she said. "If the Jews of Persia die, I must die with them. For I am a Jewess and I do not care to live if my people die."

Ahasuerus was very angry. He called for his soldiers to take Haman to his death.

"O king," said one of the servants, "in Haman's courtyard stands a high gallows on which he planned to hang Mordecai tomorrow."

"Let him be hanged on the gallows which he built for that good man," commanded the king. "And bring Mordecai before me."

Ahasuerus gave to Mordecai the royal ring Haman had worn. Then Mordecai in the king's name sent out letters to every great city and small town in Persia.

These letters said that now the people must obey Mordecai instead of the wicked Haman and that no Jew should be hurt in all the land.

The Jews in Persia gave thanks to God for saving them from death. They praised Esther and Mordecai who now received all the honors which the king had given Haman.

When Haman planned to kill all the Jews he had drawn lots to find a lucky day. The Persian word for lot is *Pur*, so the day on which the Jews were saved from Haman is called *Purim*, the Day of the Drawing of Lots. In our own time Jews still keep the holiday as they did in faraway Persia so long ago. They give each other presents, and send food and clothing to the poor, and sing happy songs. And in their synagogues they read again the old, old story of how Queen Esther saved her people.